THE ROCKS OF ANGLESEY'S COAST

First published in 2013

ISBN: 978-1-84524-209-1

Cover design: Carreg Gwalch

Published by Gwasg Carreg Gwalch,
12 Iard yr Orsaf, Llanrwst, Wales LL26 0EH
tel: 01492 642031
fax: 01492 641502
email: books@carreg-gwalch.com
website: www.carreg-gwalch.com

The rocks of Anglesey's coast

by
Jack E. Treagus & Susan H. Treagus

Contents

Introduction

Anglesey (Ynys Môn) contains within a small area probably the greatest variety of rocks in the British Isles, ranging from nearly 700 million years old to deposits from the last Ice Age. There are metamorphic, sedimentary and igneous rocks, structures such as folds and faults, fossils and minerals, and interesting glacial deposits and landforms. Anglesey's coastline reveals these rocks in unrivalled clarity, and will be seen – even if not understood – by many visitors to the beautiful beaches and cliff paths of this island. We have spent many happy hours on the rocks of Anglesey, together, from our student days, through careers as geologists, and now into retirement (Figure 1). As structural geologists, we have been interested to unravel the history of the older rocks and their structures, but our motive in writing this book is to enable visitors, walkers and amateur geologists to appreciate the beautiful rocks of Anglesey at a simple level.

*1. The authors on the coastal path on quartzite near Rhoscolyn Head (excursion **F**). Photograph by Peter Hudleston.*

Anglesey recently achieved UNESCO 'Geopark' status, through the work of dedicated local geologists, especially Margaret Wood at Llansadwrn, in setting up GeoMôn (http://www.geomon.co.uk/). This Geopark status is a formal recognition of the importance of Anglesey's geology, worldwide. The GeoMôn website provides information for the public on Anglesey's geology, and on timetabled activities, and their visitor centre at Amlwch Port is worth a visit for its displays and publications for purchase.

The first descriptions of Anglesey's rocks were in the early nineteenth century, the result of short visits by amateur naturalists, but it was not until the work of Edward Greenly in the later part of the century that systematic geological mapping was employed on the island. Greenly's exquisite 1" to the mile geological map is now available from the British Geological Survey, unaltered, at the scale of 1:50:000, and interested readers are urged to purchase or consult it. In Figure 2 we reproduce this map in simplified form.

The Ordnance Survey 1:50,000 Anglesey map (Landranger 114) is really essential for location, and the two 1:25,000 topographic maps that cover the island (Explorer 262 and 263), are a great additional benefit. The six-figure National Grid references that we give for our localities can be read from these maps; they all lie within the 100km grid square SH, so these letters are omitted. For a more detailed geological description of some of the localities listed here, we recommend the 2008 book by Jack Treagus: "Anglesey Geology – a Field Guide" (published by GeoMôn – see above). For a specific guide to the rocks along the Anglesey coastal path, see "Rocks and Landscapes of the Anglesey Coastal Footpath by John Conway (2010, published by GeoMôn). For a more comprehensive account of the geology of Anglesey, the reader is referred to the British Geological Survey Regional Geology Guide "Wales (New Edition)".

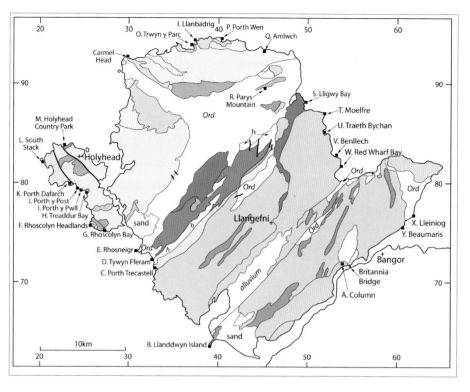

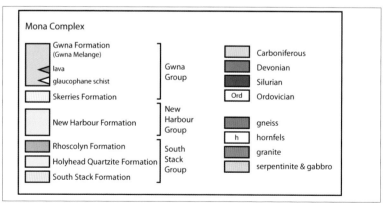

Mona Complex

Gwna Formation (Gwna Melange)		
lava	Gwna Group	
glaucophane schist		
Skerries Formation		
New Harbour Formation	New Harbour Group	
Rhoscolyn Formation	South Stack Group	
Holyhead Quartzite Formation		
South Stack Formation		

Carboniferous
Devonian
Silurian
Ord — Ordovician

gneiss
h — hornfels
granite
serpentinite & gabbro

2. *Simplified geological map of Anglesey, locating excursions **A – Y**, and important place names. Drawn by Richard Hartley.*
A larger version is printed on the back cover fold-out.

We have set out this book as a series of 25 excursions, lettered **A** to **Y**, going round Anglesey's coast roughly clockwise from the Britannia Bridge entry from mainland N Wales (Figure 2). Two excursions (**A** and **R**) are *not* on the coast, but are included because of their importance. Most of the excursions involve a round-trip walk of less than 2 km, and some are sufficiently close together, and related, to make a longer combined excursion. Only two excursions involve longer walks from suitable parking, making these substantial excursions: **Llandwyn Island, Newborough (B)** (front cover), where the first exposures are 1.5 km from the carpark, and the total excursion requires a 6 km walk; and **Rhoscolyn Headlands (F)** (Figure 1), on Holy Island, which amounts to about 5 km. Most of our localities are on shore rocks or safe cliff-tops, chosen as places where visitors would naturally go, and there is no need to descend anywhere precipitous. There is always a danger of missed footing, as with any coastal walking, so sturdy footwear and weather-proof clothing are advised. The need to pay attention to tidal predictions and weather forecasts cannot be emphasised too greatly, as we recommend low tide for some of the excursions.

In our descriptions of the sedimentary rock types that will be encountered on each excursion, we have confined ourselves to commonly-used sedimentary terms such as "sandstones" and "mudstones", and, where appropriate, the names of the equivalent metamorphic rocks. With igneous rocks we try to confine ourselves to more familiar terms such as granite, lava, and dyke. All less familiar geological names are shown in *italics*, when first used, and are explained in the *Glossary* at the end of this book.

Anglesey's rocks and geological events
In the geological history of the island given below, we show in bold the place-names for the excursions shown on Figure 2, that comprise the subsequent chapters of the book. The geology is, of course, described for each excursion, but here we summarise the

rocks found on Anglesey and shown in Figure 2, from oldest to youngest, together with the main geological and tectonic events.

The oldest known rocks on Anglesey are a body of granite and adjacent *gneiss*, that form the NE-SW belt in its centre (Figure 2). Known as the **Coedana Granite** and the **Coedana gneiss complex**, their ages have been determined from *radiometric dating*: the *granite* is 614 million years old, but the *gneiss* is 670 Ma, placing both in the Precambrian. Sometimes described as the crystalline basement to Anglesey, it is clear from these ages that the Coedana granite intruded the older gneiss. The gneiss can be seen at **Porth Trecastell (C)** and **Tywyn Fferam (D)** and is a pale grey *quartz-feldspar-muscovite* rock. The Coedana granite, whose main exposure is inland and not easily accessible, can be seen as veins and inclusions in the gneiss at **Tywyn Fferam (D)**, as well as pebbles on nearby beaches. The granite exhibits a great variety of colours but is typically a pink coarse-grained quartz-feldspar-muscovite-*biotite* rock.

The next oldest rocks are known as the **Mona Complex**, a term coined by Greenly for the metamorphic rocks that occupy 75% of the ground surface of Anglesey (Figure 2). These rocks, (also known as the Monian Supergroup) form an even greater percentage of the coastal exposure, of exceptional quality and accessibility, and of great interest to us, particularly on Holy Island. The coastal outcrops of Mona Complex vary from low-lying and easily accessible cliffs with pleasant sandy bays (see cover photo), to impressive wave-swept towering cliffs (Figures 1 & 3). The rocks have great variety, and different rocks and features can be seen on excursions **A – B**, and **F – O**, on the west and north coastline.

As the map in Figure 2 illustrates, there are several distinct areas of the Mona Complex, and a variety of rock names and rock types, separated by areas of non-exposure, or younger formations or *faults*. The stratigraphically lowest part of the Mona Complex is

3. Spectacular coastal rocks and scenery on Rhoscolyn Headlands (F), with accessible folds in the core of the Rhoscolyn Anticline. Photograph by Peter Hudleston.

the **South Stack Group**, a sequence of metamorphosed sandstones and mudstones (now *quartzites* and *schists*) with local *conglomerate*, that were deposited as sand-rich *turbidite* fans in a sedimentary basin. This Group is divided into three formations: the **South Stack Formation**, the **Holyhead Quartzite Formation**, and the **Rhoscolyn Formation**, all comprising substantial beds of sandstone and minor mudstone, forming dramatic coastal scenery, as seen at **Rhoscolyn Headlands (F)** (Figure 3), **Porth Dafarch (K)**, **South Stack (L)**, and **Holyhead Country Park (M)**. The overlying *New Harbour Group/Formation* has a different appearance, dominantly consisting of silvery green *schists* that were once thinly-bedded mud and silt layers, with a thin unit of volcanic *tuff* at its base. These rocks, dominated by small-scale folding are seen at

12

*4. Small-scale folds in the New Harbour Formation schists at Porth y Pwll (**I**).*

Rhoscolyn, Treaddur Bay, Porth y Pwll (Figure 4), and **Porth y Post (F – J)**. The natural junction of the Rhoscolyn Formation and overlying New Harbour Formation is seen best in **Rhoscolyn Bay (G)**.

The most dramatic aspect of the lower rocks of the Mona Complex is the folding they have undergone, possibly the best-displayed anywhere in the British Islands. The large-scale *folds* of beds of metamorphosed sandstones and mudstones, tens of metres across are particularly well-displayed on the cliffs of Holy Island at **Rhoscolyn (F & G)** (Figure 3), **Porth Dafarch (K)** and at **South Stack (L)**. Smaller-scale folds in the more finely layered New Harbour Formation, only metres to centimetres across, are seen best around the coastline of **Treaddur Bay (H)**, **Porth y Pwll (I)** (Figure 4) and **Porth y Post (J)**.

On northern Anglesey, the rocks attributed to the New Harbour Formation in Figure 2 are locally known as the ***Amlwch Beds***, as seen at **Amlwch (Q)**. These are finely bedded rocks, and hence are usually correlated with the New Harbour Formation seen on Holy Island, although we cannot provide definitive evidence for this. The rocks shown in Figure 2 as **Skerries Formation** are a medley of gritty rocks and volcanic tuff, that some geologists consider to be a lateral variety of New Harbour Formation, but most attribute to the lowermost Gwna Group, described next. Skerries Formation *schists* can be seen at **Porth Wen (P)**.

The upper parts of the Mona Complex is known as the **Gwna Group** (Figure 2) and it outcrops in large areas in the southeast, centre and west of Anglesey, and smaller areas in the north. It can be seen best on the west coast at **Llanddwyn Island, Newborough (B)**, and on the north coast at **Trwyn y Parc, Cemaes (N)** and **Llanbadrig (O)**. The rocks in this Gwna Group are very varied, including *pillow lavas* dramatically exposed at **Llanddwyn Island, Newborough (B)**, and *glaucophane schist* (blue schist) at the **Llanfair P.G. Column (A)**, but the bulk of this rock group were originally sandstones and mudstones, now schists, as seen at **Beaumaris (Y)**. A spectacular jumbled mixture of these rocks, known as the **Gwna Melange**, involving oceanic volcanic rocks, *cherts*, mudstones, limestone and sandstones, is seen at **Llanddwyn Island, Newborough (B)** and **Llanbadrig (O)**. These Gwna Group rocks are generally less strongly folded and less complexly deformed than those of the South Stack, and New Harbour Groups, but all these Mona Complex rocks have been compressed as a result of continental and sea floor movements of the Earth's *tectonic plates* at this time, as part of the *Caledonian Orogeny*. In particular, the dragging down, or *subduction*, of parts of the crust is strikingly witnessed on Anglesey by the rare blue amphibole mineral, *glaucophane*, that form the blue schists seen at the **Llanfair P.G. Column (A)**; the minerals in these rocks are known to have suffered extremely high pressures.

The Mona Complex rocks contain no fossils of definitive age. Worm tubes probably of early Cambrian age have been found in the South Stack Formation, but not visited in these excursions. Stromatolites (laminated algal mats) and acritarchs (single cell algae), also of probable early Cambrian age, are seen in the limestone in the *melange* at **Trwyn y Parc, Cemaes (N)** and **Llanbadrig (O)**. A *radiometric age* of 522 million years has been obtained from zircon crystals from the South Stack Formation at **South Stack (L)**, placing these rocks as early Cambrian. Parts of the Mona Complex are overlain *unconformably* by fossiliferous Ordovician sediments, described next. Folding on axes that are NE-SW-trending, with steep axial plane cleavage, affect both the Mona Complex (its first phase of folding), as seen so well at **Rhoscolyn Headlands (F)**, and also the Ordovician rocks discussed next. This is the typical trend of the *Caledonian Orogeny*; we will consider the age of this deformation later.

The most accessible exposures of **Ordovician rocks** are at **Rhosneigr (E)** (Figure 2). Here are exceptionally well-displayed folds of sandstone beds in mudstone (see cover photograph and Figure 5) with steep *axial plane cleavage*, as well as underlying *conglomerates*. Ordovician conglomerates are also seen on the north coast at **Porth Wen (P)**, with an *unconformity* onto underlying Gwna Group rocks. Ordovician mudstones also occur together with Silurian rocks, at **Parys Mountain (R)**. *Graptolites* have been found in all these Ordovician rocks (but not by the present writers) that date them as Arenig. These rocks, with their conglomerates and subsequent deeper water mudstones, are considered to mark a marine transgression that occurred throughout Britain 470 million years ago.

The **Silurian rocks** on Anglesey are only known from the outcrops associated with the volcanic rocks and mineralization in the superb old inland quarry exposures that make up the dramatic feature of **Parys Mountain (R)**. The Silurian rocks are shales and siltstones of Llandovery age (440 Ma), and *graptolites* can be

*5. Folds in Ordovician sandstone and mudstone in beach-side rocks at Rhosneigr (**E**).*

found, but the area is most notable for its mineralization, *chalcopyrite, pyrite, zinc blende* and *galena* minerals that were first mined during the Bronze Age and the Roman period. However, the visible effects of mining here date mainly from the 18th century, when copper mining dominated, and **Porth Amlwch (Q)** became its port of export.

All of the rocks of Ordovician and Silurian age, together with the older Mona Complex rocks, are affected by a period of deformation in the late Silurian, known as the ***Caledonian Orogeny***. This, produced the spectacular folds and cleavages seen in the supposed Cambrian South Stack Group and New Harbour Formation seen on all the Holy Island excursions (**F – M**), and also in the Ordovician rocks at **Rhosneigr (E)** and the Ordovician-Silurian at **Parys Mountain (R)**. Major *faults* are seen at **Rhoscolyn Headlands (F)** and **Holyhead Country Park (M)**, formed at a later stage in the orogeny as they postdate the major folds. The

Caledonian folds and axial plane cleavage trend NE, and have been attributed to closure of tectonic plates when the ancient ocean that preceded the Atlantic, named Iapetus, closed in the late Silurian, about 425 million years ago.

Devonian rocks are well-exposed on the east coast of Anglesey at the north side of **Lligwy Bay** (**S**). These red-coloured sedimentary rocks, mostly siltstones and sandstones, in part calcareous, are dramatically folded and locally cleaved. No body fossils have been recovered from these rocks but there is plentiful evidence of organic burrowing. Sedimentary features such as sun-cracks and *cross-bedding* indicate that these were river deposits with periods of emergence in desert-like conditions. We consider the *folds*, weak *cleavage* and *faults* in these Devonian rocks to be effects of the *Acadian Orogeny* in the mid-Devonian, about 400 million years ago. These structures probably formed at the same time as the major Carmel Head *thrust* fault complex on N Anglesey, driving Mona Complex rocks southwards over Ordovician and Silurian rocks, as shown in the geological map pattern (Figure 2).

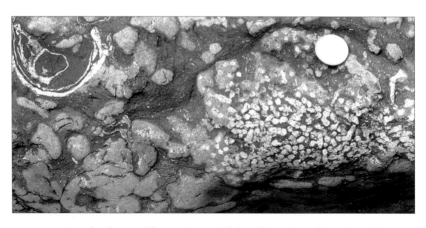

*6. Coral colony, Lithostrotion, with brachiopods in bioturbated Carboniferous limestone at Traeth Bychan (**U**).*

Carboniferous rocks are extensively exposed in the east of the island, where sandy bays from Lligwy, Moelfre, Traeth Bychan, Benllech and Red Wharf, are popular with visitors and are the location of many camping and caravan sites. The limestone cliffs of these bays provide excellent exposures of the generally flat-lying fossiliferous limestones and mudstones with coral reefs, that developed in tropical seas at this time, seen at **Moelfre (T)**, **Traeth Bychan (U)**, and **Benllech (V)**. Fossils of *brachiopods*, *corals* and *crinoids* are seen particularly well at **Traeth Bychan (U)** (Figure 6) and at **Moelfre (T)**, the latter also being a good place to see *karst* weathering and landscape in the Carboniferous limestone. Carboniferous sandstones interbedded with limestones can be seen at **Red Wharf Bay (W)**, and here there is also evidence that the limestones developed on a Carboniferous coastal

*7. Shore exposures of pipes and plugs in the Carboniferous at Red Wharf Bay (**W**), also glacially striated and overlain by till.*

shelf that underwent episodes of exposure during which pot-holes were formed and filled with sandstones and pebbles from rivers. These "fossil" pot-holes, rarely preserved in Britain, are up to 3m wide and 5m deep, and are well-exposed on an accessible foreshore (Figure 7).

No solid sedimentary rocks of **Mesozoic** age are known on Anglesey. The only **Cenozoic** sedimentary rocks are **Miocene** (60 Ma) sediments that infilled pot-holes that formed within the Mona Complex Gwna Group limestone at this time, dramatically exposed at **Trwyn y Parc, Cemaes** (**N**).

The landscape subsequently would have been fashioned between the **Permo-Triassic** and the **Pleistocene** when the next significant depositional landforms were formed. Anglesey was probably overrun by ice during the four periods of glaciation affecting upland Britain during the **Quaternary**, but the main evidence of a glacial event on Anglesey is from around 20,000 years ago. At this time Anglesey was completely covered with ice, predominantly by an ice stream from the northeast, for which there is an exceptional range of evidence. Evidence of ice movement from *glacial striae* that are usually NE-SW directed can be seen on many of the limestone pavements on eastern Anglesey that are overlain by boulder clay known as *till*, such as the *Irish Bay Till* seen at **Red Wharf Bay** (**W**) (Figure 7). A *roche moutonnée* and glacial striae can be seen, together with boulder clay, on the west coast at **Tywyn Fferam** (**D**). At **Lleiniog** (**X**), the Menai Straits coastal section reveals exceptional detail of Quaternary sediments and structures developed in a river in front of a retreating glacier. Most of this evidence is for the last Ice Age, at about 20,000 years, but at **Red Wharf Bay** (**W**), *raised beach* deposits are also preserved from an earlier glaciation in the mid-Pleistocene, about 125,000 years ago.

Anglesey also contains some interesting **igneous geology**. The intrusive Precambrian Coedana *granite*, seen as pebbles and veins at **Tywyn Fferam (D)**, was mentioned earlier, as one of the oldest rocks on Anglesey. Other igneous rocks, contemporary with the sediments, and mentioned above, are the *tuffs* in the New Harbour Group at **Rhoscolyn Bay (G)** and the *pillow lavas*, and other volcanic rocks such as *agglomerate* in the Gwna Group at **Llanddwyn Island, Newborough (B)**. Some basic and ultrabasic intrusive rocks (*gabbro* and *serpentinite*) occur in scattered inland exposures of the New Harbour Group on Holy Island. Although not suitable for inclusion in this book, an assortment of these *gabbros* and *serpentinites* can be seen as large beach defence boulders at **Treaddur Bay (H)**. In the Ordovician rocks at **Parys Mountain (R)**, the mineralization is associated with igneous activity, including *rhyolite* lava and volcanic sediments.

8. *Dolerite dyke intruded into Gwna schists at Beaumaris (Y), with small fault across the centre, and a set of diagonal joints.*

There are two distinct swarms of *dolerite dykes* on Anglesey. One is associated with the end of the *Caledonian Orogeny*, about 420 million years ago, related to the closing of the pre-Atlantic Iapetus ocean. Dolerite dykes of this age are especially well-seen at **Beaumaris (Y)** (Figure 8), and also at **Holyhead Country Park (M)**. The other set of dykes is of lower *Cenozoic* age (formerly known as the Tertiary dyke swarm), and is associated with the opening of the North Atlantic about 40-60 million years ago. Well-displayed Cenozoic dolerite dykes can be seen at **Porth y Post (J)** and **Porth Dafarch (K)**. Both swarms trend generally NW-SE and the dykes usually exhibit *spheroidal weathering*.

The present day landscape of Anglesey and its coastline is due to many processes over its geological and geographical history. The Menai Straits marks not just today's boundary between mainland North Wales and Anglesey, but is a major fault system that has been an active boundary from the Cambrian right through to present-day. This explains why the Precambrian-Cambrian rocks on Anglesey (the Mona Complex) are different from those of equivalent age in north Wales (the famous Cambrian slates). They were deposited in different sedimentary basins that may at that time have been some distance apart. The Menai Strait fault system is one of many important faults that created the Anglesey of today; another is the NE-trending Berw Fault 8 km to the north, that created a scarp and wide depression from Malltraeth to Red Wharf Bay, noted on the way to **Llanddwyn Island, Newborough (B)**. Dominant NW-trending faults cut through Holy Island (Figure 2), bounding the landmark Holyhead Mountain seen at the **Holyhead Country Park (M)**, and creating the deep coastal gullies that characterise **Rhoscolyn Headlands (F)**.

The Carboniferous coast of eastern Anglesey from south Lligwy through to Red Wharf Bay provides some spectacular coastal scenery, with expansive coastal platforms of almost horizontal limestone beds that make it so suitable for caravans, campers and walkers. These rocks display remarkably regular patterns of *joints*, sometimes in two crossing sets with a criss-cross or rhombic pattern on bedding planes. They create many stretches of coastal cliffs that have a saw-tooth pattern, emphasised by local cliff falls. These joints have provided pathways for solution weathering, resulting in caves such as at **Benllech (V)**, and the karst landscape and limestone pavements, as seen at **Moelfre (T)**.

Man has also played a part in carving the present-day landscape of Anglesey. Former quarries dominate the Carboniferous limestone coastline, as seen for example at **Red Wharf Bay (W)**. This Anglesey limestone was used for building many monuments and castles over the ages. Quarrying of quartzite was also important in the past, used as a building material and for refractory bricks, and now leaving areas of industrial heritage at **Porth Wen (P)** and **Holyhead Country Park (M)**. Today, **Parys Mountain (R)** provides a colourful landscape, extraction of copper here leaving a considerable mark on the environment, and to the development of **Amlwch (Q)** as a port. It might be said that although Anglesey is no longer so active in its industry, its rocks and beach pebbles still provide wealth: the wealth of information for teachers and researchers in geology, that will help future generations understand how our Earth evolved.

A. Llanfair P.G. Column

This short excursion is to see rare blue-schists below the Marquess of Anglesey's Column at Llanfairpwllgwyngyllgogerychwyrndrobwllllantysiliogogogoch. Usually abbreviated to Llanfairpwll or Llanfair P.G., this village with its famously long name has been a settlement from the Neolithic period (4,000-2,000 BC), but its long name was created in the 19th Century, in order to attract tourists to stop on their travels on the newly opened Chester to Holyhead railway line. It worked! Llanfair P.G. entered the record books, and tourists are still attracted to the working railway station with the impossibly long name, and its associated shopping outlets and café, about 1 km to the west of this locality at [534715].

1. View of the landmark Marques of Anglesey's Column from the south. The path to the exposures is between the wooden fences.

The landmark Marquess of Anglesey's Column at Llanfair P.G. at [534715] (Figure 1), is a 27m pillar built of Carboniferous limestone from Moelfre, a coastal village on the north-east coast of Anglesey. It was erected in 1816-17 as a tribute to the Marquess, Henry Paget (1768-1854), who lost a leg at the battle of Waterloo. You can climb up 115 steps to the top (for a small charge), where there are spectacular views of Snowdonia and the beautiful Anglesey countryside.

The Anglesey monument stands on a rocky hill that was a hillfort in ancient times, but is now bluebell woods popular with walkers. The rock is part of the Gwna Group of the Mona Complex, but its interest to geologists is that it is *glaucophane schist*, known as a blue-schist because of the blue colour of the amphibole mineral, glaucophane. This metamorphic mineral forms under unusual conditions of high pressure and low temperature, and is usually attributed to metamorphism associated with a downgoing oceanic plate margin or in a subduction zone. This blue-schist has been radiometrically argon – dated to 560-550 Ma, which is near the top of the Precambrian. Some geologists consider this part of Anglesey – including the rocks on the nearby Newborough/Llandwyn Island excursion – is the remains of an ancient *subduction* zone that preserves oceanic *tectonic plate* rocks, and that these blue-schists are metamorphosed basalts from a Precambrian ocean floor.

This occurrence of glaucophane schist on Anglesey is one of the rare places in Britain where blue schists are exposed. Under most light conditions in this woodland area, the rocks will not appear dramatically blue, but a very dark grey or bluish-grey schist; and the blue glaucophane crystals will not be obvious unless a hand lens is used and the light is good. It is a protected (SSSI) location, so hammering and sampling are not allowed. However, there are many exposures close to paths in the public area of woodland below the monument, and close to a free car park.

From the Britannia Bridge, take the first exit signed A4080 and then turn left on the A5 signed for Llanfairpwllgwyngyll and Newborough. Just after a large signpost indicating a left junction to Newborough, and about 150m before (east of) this junction, take a right turn into a track leading to the car park for the Anglesey Monument (Figure 1). Approaching from the Llanfair P.G. direction, there is a sign left for the Monument just before the left turn into the car park.

2. Blocks of glaucophane schist in wall, which have a bluish tinge in sunlight.

Walk from the car park up the path bounded by wooden fences shown in Figure 1, leading uphill into the woods. At the end of the fences, a stone wall made of local blue schist blocks marks the start of the woodland area (Figure 2). These blocks are cleaner and bluer-looking than the weathered natural exposures you will see in the woods above; but if examining them, be careful not to move the blocks or disturb the wall. About 50m upwards from here, the path diverges: take the left branch. A large boulder-shaped rock outcrop in trees to the right of the path is the first natural exposure. It is very green-coloured, due to algae and mosses coating its surface in the shaded moist woodland conditions. Despite this coating, it is possible to make out a fine-grained dark blue-grey banded schist, and the presence of many small scale *folds* that have a *mineral lineation* parallel to their *axes* (Figure 3). If you can glimpse exposures of rock caught in the sunshine between the trees, you will see that it is indeed bluish coloured, as hinted in Figure 2.

3. *Glaucophane schists in the woods below the Anglesey monument, showing small folds; pencil parallel to fold axes and mineral lineation. The 'blue schists' appear green due to lichen in this woodland setting.*

About 50m before the steps to the Column, and the rocky cliffs on which it is built, turn right on a path that takes you past several mossy or ivy-covered exposure on either side, some showing folding in the blue-schists, others finer-grained and more uniform in appearance. As the path turns downhill, and before 5 steps, branch left (NE) to follow a narrower path near the base of the cliffs. These consist of blue-black glaucophane schist, containing quartz-pegmatite bands. This brings you to the base of the steps to the monument, where you can proceed upwards (there is an entrance fee) to enjoy spectacular views across southern Anglesey, the Menai Straits and its Britannia and Menai Bridges, and to Snowdonia beyond.

B. Llanddwyn Island, Newborough

Llanddwyn Island is at the southernmost tip of Anglesey, connected by a narrow strip of land (except at high tide) to Newborough Forest and the sands of Newborough Warren. The area forms an extensive nature reserve, with forest, ecologically important sand dunes and wide-open beaches. The Island, with its stunning coastal topography, protected wildlife including red squirrels and ravens, ancient lighthouses, and superb views across to Snowdonia and the Lleyn Peninsula (Figure 1), has become one of the most popular areas for walkers and naturalists on Anglesey. If this were not enough, the rocks on Llanddwyn Island are among the most dramatic and colourful to be found anywhere on Anglesey. We shall see rocks from the Gwna Group (Figure 2): volcanic lava that was expelled in blobs from vents on an ocean floor about 600 million years ago, mixed in a jumble of

1. Scenic view from the south end of Llanddwyn Island looking SE, showing the beaches, rocky shoreline, and the Old Lighthouse, with the Snowdonia – Lleyn mountain range in the background.

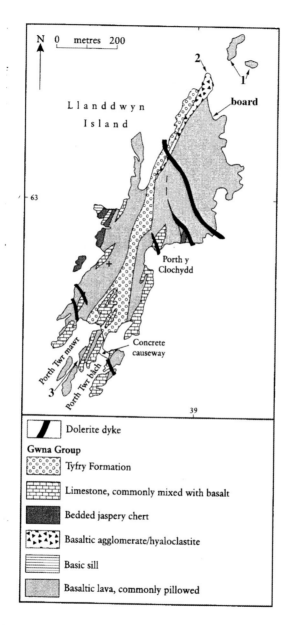

2. *Simplified geological map of Llanddwyn Island, showing the rock types and three key localities. (+ marks the ruined church of St Dwynwen.)*

muds, sands and limestones, as a result of movement of the ocean floor. The surrounding Newborough Forest and Warren are ecologically important areas of sand dunes, blown sands and wild grasses, and Newborough town grew to prominence in the past for its mat weaving from the marram grass.

For this area you will need to know the tide times, as the island may be cut off by a shallow channel for up to an hour either side of high tide, depending on tidal and weather conditions. Hammering and rock collecting are totally banned on the island. The island is an important nature reserve for nesting birds and there are restrictions on access to the shoreline in the months of March to August. Dogs are banned from the beach and island.

From the Britannia Bridge continue on the A55 for 6km and take exit 7 signposted to Gaerwen. Turn right at the roundabout to join the A5; then in approximately 2km within the village of Pentre Berw turn left on the B4419, signposted to Newborough. This road runs just to the SE of a major fault, the Berw Fault, that is responsible for a major depression across Anglesey, now occupied by the Afon Cefni and Malltraeth marshes. From this road, you will have stunning views towards the south of the island and across to Snowdonia, and in the other direction, across to the north and west of Anglesey. After about 5 km, at Llangaffo, this road becomes the B4421 to Newborough, reaching the main A4080 coastal road in Newborough village after a further 3 km. Turn left on the A4080, and after just 200m, turn right at crossroads, following a blue P sign, and a brown signpost to Llys Rhosyr. Staying on this road, passing signs to Llanddwyn parking and to the beach, in 1.5km this road ends at a Forestry Commission toll barrier (£3 payment made by coins in a slot), after which you can drive a further 2.5 km to a large car park at the coast. The car park has toilets and sometimes refreshments. From here either walk 1.5km west along the sandy shoreline, or take the signposted track through the forest, to just before the causeway to Llanddwyn Island (Figure 2, locality 1).

3. Pillow lavas at locality 1 in Figure 2, looking NE. The notebook (15cm) marks the indentation of the top of one pillow into the one above, which is to its right here as the rocks are vertical.

The most dramatic exposures of the excursion are those of *basalt pillow lavas* (Figure 3) on prominent beach outcrops northeast of the island [392636], some of which are always visible even at high tide. The pillow shapes are the result of high temperature lava coming into contact with cold water and separating into these isolated sacks up to a metre across, the margins of which quickly chilled. Then, as they settled in deep water, the higher pillows were moulded around those beneath, giving bun-shapes with curved tops and indented bases. The originally flat-lying pillows have here been rotated into a near-vertical attitude by the sideways forces as a result of the Caledonian Orogeny, so that the rounded tops now point to the SE. The centres of some of the pillows are full of gas cavities called *vesicles*, some mineral-filled, and between the pillows it is possible to see patches of blood-red *jasper*, that were originally deep-sea *chert* (silica mud), together with veins and patches of white quartz and calcite and green *epidote* minerals originating from precipitation from volcanic fluids.

Cross to the causeway and aim for the nearest rocks on the northern tip of the island (Figure 2, locality 2) at [391634]. Near a flight of steps up the cliff, there is an outcrop in a small bay of a type of volcanic breccia called *agglomerate*. Angular fragments of lava, from cms to ms across, have been blown out of a volcano, and have fallen into a fine matrix of volcanic ash. Now walk across to the large notice-board to the east (Figure 2), where there is a good display illustrating the origin of the pillow lavas, which are also exposed extensively on the northeast coastal tip of the island.

Take the main path SSW that traverses the Island for about 1 km, bringing you to the southernmost peninsulas and lighthouses (see Figure 1 and front cover picture). Continue past the ruined church of St Dwynwen and a prominent Cross on a mound, where you may be able to see to your right some prominent limestone beds, in a breccia-like mixture with basalt and volcanic *tuff*. You will see more of this rock mixture when you reach the end of the Island. Walk on until you reach the Pilots' cottages (in which there is a good little museum concerning the history of the Island) and pass the Old Lighthouse shown in Figure 1, until you reach the centre of the beach at the southern end of the Island [386625] shown as locality 3 in Figure 2. The shore exposures here are an extraordinary assortment of colourful rocks – green/blue/grey/pink mudstones and sandstones mixed with black volcanic agglomerates and tuffs, blood-red jasper, pink manganese-rich carbonate as well as pure white limestones (Figure 4). It is difficult to guide you to particular exposures as there is such a jumble of these rocks, including pillowed and brecciated basalt, in some of which you may see vesicles, small holes from which gas escaped.

4. View of the variety of rocks described as melange, on beaches on the S end of Llanddwyn Island, looking east with the Old Lighthouse for location; see also Figure 1. Photo courtesy of Paul Kabrna.

On the SE side of the bay there are more tuffs and agglomerates that contain fragments of fine-grained igneous rocks and pink grits, and pillow lavas with jasper (Figure 5). If you go through a gully at the SE corner of the beach (needs at least medium tide) you will see an even more colourful scene of pillowed basalts crossed by a dark dolerite dyke. This vertical sheet, typically only a metre or two wide, intruded the pillowed basalt by lava at a later time. Follow the dyke into the next cove where there is well-exposed jumble of limestone and pink quartzite blocks. This is where the famous geologist Edward Greenly, who first mapped these rocks in the 1890s, originally used the term *melange* for this type of mixture of rocks, and called these rocks Gwna Melange. Melanges are now thought to be the result of chaotic

*5. Jasper surrounding pillow-like shapes of basalt, veined by calcite,
near locality 3 in Figure 2.*

movement of rocks on the sea floor as a result of earthquake activity, or massive debris slides down continental slopes. This melange contains a lot of ocean-floor rocks, such as pillow basalts and cherts. You will be able to see another melange on the Llanbadrig excursion, on the northern coast of Anglesey.

You can return to the entrance of the Island via a different path past a ruined church, along the west side of the island, giving good views of the southwest coast of Anglesey. You will then be able to view, from a distance, a variety of coastal outcrops on the western side of Llanddwyn Island (see Figure 2), including agglomerates, and some striking red beds of jaspery chert and tuffs oriented vertically, in the same steep orientation of bedding as the pillow lavas seen at the beginning. All these rocks have been rotated from originally horizontal into vertical on the western limb of a large syncline identified in this area, probably part of the Caledonian orogenic event.

C. Porth Trecastell

This is a large sandy beach, well-used in the holiday season and at fine weekends, and would fit in well with the excursion to Rhosneigr and with the excursion to Tywyn Fferam a km to the north. From the Britannia Bridge continue on the A55 across Anglesey for about 18km to exit 5 for the A4080, signposted Rhosneigr. Follow this road for about 5km, and after the village of Llanfaelog, follow the signs for Abberffraw. In 2 km you will pass a car park for Tywyn Fferam on the right (see next excursion). In another kilometre, on the right, there is the car

1. Cliffs of Coedana gneiss just south of the stream inlet towards the south side of Porth Trecastell, looking SW, showing inlets on the south side (right background). The grey gneiss and network of white quartz veins (shown in close up in Figure 2) are cleanly exposed in the lower half of the picture, whereas, the rock above is shattered by fractures, and brown-weathered.

2. Closer view of the grey gneiss in the cliffs of Figure 1, looking east, showing ribbon structure and quartz bands and veins. The gneiss banding dips moderately S, and a subhorizontal fault runs across the picture.

park for Porth Trecastell, marked only by a street sign (Porth Trecastell) low on the roadside wall to the right of the entrance. This large free car park, at [334708], has a useful information point, but no toilets.

The bay is also called Cable Bay after the installation here of one of the first undersea telephone cables in 1855, to Ireland. However, the geological attraction are the cliffs of *gneiss*, seen best on the first cliffs towards the south side of the bay [334707] (Figure 1). The rock has a ribbon structure which is composed of bands of coarse-grained *quartz* (pale white) bands containing some *feldspar* (pink), cms to mms thick, alternating with bands of finer quartz and *muscovite* (Figure 2). It has no indication of any original bedding structure and is criss-crossed by later quartz veins. It is typical of a zone of gneiss, known as the Coedana gneiss complex, which stretches NE across Anglesey towards Red Wharf Bay. In the centre of Anglesey these rocks are apparently intruded by, and therefore older than, the Coedana *granite*. The granite had been dated at 614 million years and the gneisses at 667 million years, apparently confirming this intrusive relationship, and indicating that these Precambrian gneisses are the oldest rocks on Anglesey. Veins of the granite can be seen intruding the gneiss in the neighbouring Tywyn Fferam excursion. The pebbles on the beach here also show good examples of the gneiss structure.

The cliffs of gneiss around Porth Trecastell are shattered with fractures – *joints* and *faults* – in steep and flat-lying orientations on many scales, with the result that the rocks are locally heavily

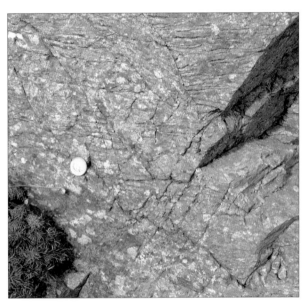

3. Small-scale faults in gneiss exposures on the north side of Porth Trecastell, looking N. The gneiss banding has a subhorizontal trace (its strike) because it is dipping S towards the viewer; the two fault sets, dipping 60° W and E, create a rhombic pattern.

weathered and brown-stained (Figure 1). The south side of the bay has some attractive inlets and stacks resulting from weathering along some of the larger fractures. The gneiss on the north side of the bay is also cut by a series of fractures, with some particularly good exposures of small-scale faults with cm-scale displacements that form two symmetrical sets (Figure 3).

It is worth taking the signed coastal footpath from the north side of the beach, onto the Mynydd Mawr headland that contains a restored 4000 year-old chambered Cairn. The gneiss here is crossed by several dolerite dykes, of Caledonian age, about 390 million years old, typically trending NW, seen on the cliff edge. Some of the dykes show a coarse crystalline texture in their centres and a finer one at their edges, where they cooled against the country rock. Here there are also good sections through the Pleistocene boulder clay that overlies the gneiss. If you were to continue on the coastal path, it would bring you down into Porth Nobla and onwards northwards from there to the exposures described in the Trwyn Fferam excursion.

D. Tywyn Fferam

This is another popular beach, especially for surfers. It would fit in well with the excursion to Rhosneigr, two kilometres to the north and with the excursion to Porth Trecastell a km to the south. From the Britannia Bridge continue on the A55 across Anglesey for about 18km to exit 5 for the A4080, signposted Rhosneigr. Follow this road for about 5km, and after the village of Llanfaelog, following the signs for Abberffraw, and in 2km use the large signposted free car park on the right, at Porth Tywyn Fferam [331716]. This car park, bordered by sand dunes, has an information point called Porth Tyn Tywyn and seasonal toilets.

1. *The roche moutonnée looking SE approaching from Tywyn Fferam, with a boulder clay cap left of the person. The rock is grey gneiss that contains inclusions and veins of granite, and top surfaces show glacial striae.*

Take the footpath past the information point, across the dunes 200m to the beach and go to large outcrops of grey *gneiss* to your left [330714]; these rocks, although at the top of the beach, are best seen at medium to low tide. The second, and most prominent outcrop, seen in Figure 1, is a good example of a *roche moutonnée* (supposedly like a sheep's back), an elongate mound carved as the ice passed over the rocks. On its top, grooved and polished surfaces give the direction of ice movement (Figure 2). The mound (Figures 1 & 3) typically has a narrow smooth end

2. *Top surface of the roche moutonnée in Figure 1, showing the glacial striae from top left to middle right, and a pink granite inclusion to the right of the pencil.*

3. *View of the roche moutonnée from the other side (looking NW), the asymmetric profile showing the ice movement was from right to left, and showing the boulder clay cap. On the immediate left, the gneiss is schistose, with vertical schistosity visible.*

indicating the direction from which the ice came, and a broader steep, rough end where the glacier plucked at the rock as it passed. In this instance it, and the *glacial striae*, are aligned NE-SW, so the ice must have been moving to the SW. On its top there is a cap, 1-2m thick, of Pleistocene boulder clay in which you will find stones from a variety of sources (Figure 3).

This mound and nearby outcrops offer the rare opportunity to examine a network of veins and boulders of *granite* within the grey gneiss (Figures 2 & 4). These are not always easy to distinguish from one another, but the granite has a distinctive pink colour owing to the presence of *feldspar* in a background of

4. *Pinkish granite sheets, subvertical and 10-20 cm wide, within the gneiss at the edge of the sea, looking westwards from the mound.*

white *quartz* crystals. On the very top of this mound (Figure 1), seaward of the boulder clay cap, there is a one exceptionally large inclusion of granite about 3m wide and 5 metres long (Figure 5). This has a more irregular, lumpy surface, compared with the ice-striated gneiss on either side. Indeed, this hard core to the roche moutonnée may be the very reason for its existence. These granite veins and inclusions, together with pebbles on the beach, suggest that we are not far from the main Coedana granite intrusion that, although having a major outcrop in the middle of Anglesey, is rather inaccessible. This granite has been dated at 614 million years and the gneisses at 667 million years, indicating that these Precambrian gneisses are the oldest rocks on Anglesey, and were intruded by the granite in the Precambrian.

5. The top of the roche moutonnée looking SSE. The central lumpy outcrop between the two notebooks is the large granite inclusion mentioned in the text. In the foreground and background are smooth ice-striated gneiss containing smaller granite inclusions and veins, such as shown in Figure 1.

The adjacent gneisses, exposed in outcrops on the beach are very variable in appearance. In places massive and elsewhere showing a vertical gneiss banding, it is often difficult to separate them from the granite inclusions that they contain. The beach is a good place to explore for a great variety of pebbles, including the gneiss and granite, as well as *schist* and bright red *jasper* (Figure 6).

6. *A sample of pebbles that can be found on the beach at this locality. The top right pebble is gneiss, the other three large pebbles are different textures of Coedana granite, with the two in the foreground having pink colour from the feldspar. The two small red pebbles below the coin are red jasper (chert).*

E. Rhosneigr

Rhosneigr is one of the main seaside villages on Anglesey, popular with holidayers and surfers, and can become busy in the summer, and at weekends. The village has a good range of shops, B&Bs and a hotel, cafes, a car park and public conveniences. The rocks that you will see on the shore and offshore islands at Rhosneigr are of early Ordovician age. Below the sea walls and the bordering beach are dark grey mudstones with sandstone beds, displaying some spectacular folds. The offshore reefs and islands (Figure 1) comprise an underlying conglomerate that forms the base of the Ordovician on Anglesey, and marks the Arenig-age marine transgression that occurred throughout Britain about 470 million years ago. These are our two localities; they are close together and do not involve much walking or scrambling, but this excursion ideally requires low tide, as the reefs of locality 1 become islands at mid to high tide.

1. Rhosneigr shore looking west, showing offshore islands (locality 1) and mudstone shore in the foreground (locality 2).

45

From the Britannia Bridge continue on the A55 across Anglesey for about 18km to the exit for the A4080, signposted Rhosneigr. Follow this road for about 5km, and after the village of Llanfaelog, follow the signs right to take you into Rhosneigr village. At the crossroads, turn left on the High Street. After about 100m, turn left following a Parking sign, taking you to the main car park that is above the Library. There are public conveniences here, open all year round (daytime).

Walk down to the High Street, turn left, and follow this road southwestwards, going past houses until you see an area of seating at the cliff top. The ground around the seats here is made up of purple slate chippings from the famous Cambrian slate belt of mainland North Wales, not a rock that is found on Anglesey. Descend to the beach from here. You will be walking down cliffs made up of dark grey mudstone and light grey sandstone that form the exposures of the second locality; but it is more logical first to cross the stony beach ridge to reach the off-shore reefs and islands shown in Figure 1, ideally at low tide,

Locality 1: offshore reefs and islands [314729]
These reefs are best to examine at their base on the shore, in a strip of clean wave-washed rocks between the high tide seaweed line, and lichen-covered exposures above (Figure 1). Here you will see that these rocks are *conglomerate* (Figure 2). They underlie the dark grey mudstones of the cliffs and main shore (Figures 1 & 3), and form the base of the Ordovician in this part of Anglesey. Regrettably, no sedimentary contact between the two rock types is exposed, but the boundary is presumed to run under the beach deposits.

The conglomerate is crowded with *clasts* of a variety of size, 1 to 10 cms across, and of a variety of compositions. The larger clasts that are mostly of quartzite are supported in a matrix of finer clasts with a gritty texture (Figure 2). This rock, of Arenig age (about 470 Ma), is thought to have accumulated by gravity debris

2. The conglomerate at locality 1. Most of the prominent clasts are quartzite, supported in a matrix of finer clasts.

flow in a deep narrow marine basin that was probably fault-bounded in this part of Anglesey at the time. The conglomerate is of great interest for understanding the state of the deformation of the older Monian rocks, such as those seen at the nearby Rhoscolyn excursions. There is evidence from the composition of pebbles that Monian rocks were being eroded and included in this conglomerate. It is easiest to examine these by looking at individual loose pebbles, derived from the conglomerate, that are abundant on the shore. There are many white *quartzite* clasts that might be Holyhead Quartzite, and some grey sandstone clasts probably derived from the nearby South Stack or Rhoscolyn Formations. The latter appear to have a grain flattening that might be the first cleavage that is seen in these rocks on Holy Island. Of particular interest are the silver-green schistose clasts that are possibly derived from the New Harbour Formation; if these clasts contain the same *schistosity* as we see at their localities on Holy Island, as appears to be the case, this could be evidence that the deformation in the Monian rocks of

Holy Island pre-dates the Arenig. On the other hand, as you will see in the overlying Ordovian rocks at locality 2, these mudstones and siltstones are strongly *folded* and contain a *slaty cleavage*, so some of the evidence of cleavage in the clasts in the conglomerate could be a result of the same Caledonian deformation. These questions remain open to debate and further study.

Walk back across the pebbly ridge to the dark grey rocks exposed below the cliff wall (Figure 3), that you crossed earlier.

3. View of Rhosneigr looking north, showing the cliffs and foreshore of locality 2, below the sea walls.

Locality 2: South end of Rhosneigr beach and cliffs [319725-317727]

Start at the southeastern end of a 100m-long section of dark grey rocks that are exposed beneath the sea wall, and on the beach [319725] (Figure 3). You will then be able to progress northwestwards and view the rocks and their *folds* in the ideal cross-sectional view, perpendicular to *fold axes* that *plunge* NE

*4. View looking northeast of an open fold in a sandstone bed,
and steep axial plane cleavage in the mudstone.*

(Figure 4). The best section runs from below the corner of the
wall to below the northeastern end of the sea wall and the start of
a fence above, where you will have easy access to rocks that are
clean and sea washed between high and low tide.

The rocks are predominantly dark grey mudstones that have been
changed into *slate* by the effects of deformation and
metamorphism during the *Caledonian Orogeny*. Their age is
presumed Arenig, on the basis of fossils found in nearby inland
exposures. Within the slate/mudstone are pale grey siltstone
beds, with thicknesses varying from 1 cm to 20 cm or more, and
many of these beds are folded (Figures 4 and 5), which
demonstrates that there has been a considerable amount of
shortening in the rocks. Overall, the "sheet-dip" of the folded
beds, as viewed down plunge in this section, is more or less
horizontal once the folds are ironed out.

5. *Tight folds in a siltstone bed with axial plane slaty cleavage in the surrounding mudstone, looking northeast.*

The slaty cleavage in the mudstones is intricately associated with the folding, and close to the orientation of the *axial-planes* to the folds, as shown in Figures 5 and 6: this is the plane perpendicular to the direction of shortening in the rocks. In some folds, *cleavage refraction* can observed from the axial-plane orientation in the slate into an orientation towards bedding-perpendicular in the folded sandstone or siltstone, with a wider spaced fractured appearance; see Figure 4, Introduction Figure 5, and Glossary Figure 2. The fanning and refraction of cleavage in folds is a characteristic feature of the different mechanical properties of the rock layers during contractional deformation: in this case, the siltstone layer has behaved as a stiffer material. The sandstone and siltstone beds also shows signs of brittle behaviour, probably late in the folding history, with many small

6. *Folds with localised thrusts in N-dipping beds of siltstone in mudstone with vertical cleavage. Some siltstone beds show graded bedding and irregular bases, indicating 'way up'.*

thrust type faults seen on fold limbs (Figure 6) or cutting across fold hinges. In contrast with the fanning cleavage in folds in siltstone beds, the NE-trending cleavage in the slate is dominantly planar and vertical and (Figures 4-6). You will be able to observe at close quarters many examples of beautiful folds, in addition to those photographed here.

Many of the siltstone beds show clear examples of graded beds from sandy bases to silty/muddy tops. Some of the bases show small-scale bulbous *load-structures* (Figure 6), whilst tops may exhibit *cross-bedding*. The mudstones can also be seen in places to contain silt-filled, 5mm-wide, horizontal and vertical worm burrows (Figure 7) derived from the siltstone tops, a sign of local *bioturbation* of the sediment. The siltstone beds show considerable thickness changes, often completely wedging out laterally. The dominance of mudstones in these sediments that overlie the conglomerates seen at locality 1, is evidence of deeper water deposition in a deepening marine basin.

These Ordovician mudstones and sandstones are also exposed as reefs on the main Rhosneigr beach at [317733], that can be reached by walking 400m around the shore, northwards. Alternatively, this part of the beach could be approached via the road to the beach from the crossroads. In these low relief intertidal shore exposures, you will be able to find more examples of spectacular folds in sandstone beds, with associated axial plane cleavage in the mudstones, with similar features to those described above for locality 2, and illustrated in Figures 4-7.

7. View looking NW of the base of a steeply dipping sandstone bed with worm burrows into the mudstone below.

F. Rhoscolyn Headlands

The coastal headlands of Rhoscolyn, on the SW corner of Holy Island, have become a world-famous geological area, visited by individual geologists and university and school parties, from the UK and also from abroad. This is one of the best areas in Britain to look at geological structures such as small-scale *folds*, and to use these to map out a large *anticline* across the area. The rocks are sandstones and mudstones from the Mona Complex, thought to be Cambrian in age, that have been compressed into folds and undergone low-grade *metamorphism* to produce *schistosity*. We describe an excursion centred on the coastal headlands and cliffs at Rhoscolyn, where the main localities can be examined in the course of a morning or afternoon, although a full day is advised to do it justice. For those who wish to have a more complete picture of the geology and structure of the Rhoscolyn area, we recommend following this excursion with the next one, to Rhoscolyn Bay.

Access to the superb cliff-line around Rhoscolyn is almost completely open, and some areas are National Trust owned. The area is popular with walkers, and apart from stunning geology and coastal geomorphology, there are abundant wild flowers and exceptional bird life, with occasional seals to be seen. The localities described do not require descent of steep cliffs, although care must be taken on the cliff tops, especially at times of strong winds. There are many deep gullies with sheer drops to the sea hidden beyond a grassy slope: approach the coastline with care.

From the Britannia Bridge take the A55 about 25km to exit 3, signposted Valley. If coming from Rhosneigr, rejoin the A55 in the Holyhead direction, and you will reach exit 3 after about 13km. Follow the A5 from the A55 roundabout to Valley (1km) where there are shops and cafes. At the traffic lights, turn left on to the B4545, signposted Trearddur Bay. After nearly 2km, you will cross the Four-Mile Bridge on to Holy Island; immediately after the bridge, fork left on to a minor road signposted Rhoscolyn. In 4km you will come to the prominent church of St. Gwenfaen, in front of which it is usually possible to park.

Walk up the lane to the right of the church, taking the footpath behind the churchyard, and across a stile to reach the track. Turn right to follow the track, which after about 1 km will bring you to a ladder stile by a locked gate. Follow the track to the prominent coastguard station with superb views along the Rhoscolyn coast

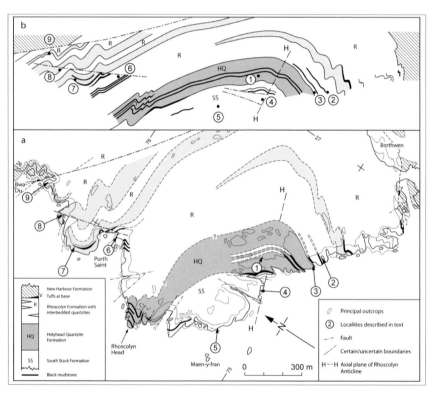

1. (a) Map of Rhoscolyn and its headlands, showing the geology and position of the 9 localities. (b) Profile cross section of the map revealing the Rhoscolyn Anticline and positions of the localities. (This is a view of the regional structure looking down the fold axis)

and, if the weather is favourable, across to Snowdonia and the Lleyn peninsula. Localities are shown on the geological map and its simplified cross section (Figure 1).

Locality 1: Coastguard Station [263752]

This locality affords a view of the whole Rhoscolyn area, and is a suitable central place to introduce the rocks and their structures. At the Coastguard Station you are at the crest of the Rhoscolyn Anticline (Figure 1), the major fold that dominates the south of Holy Island. This anticline is, in our opinion, the most accessible and well-exposed *major fold* in the whole of the British Isles: despite its deceptively simple geometry, in detail it reveals quite complicated small-scale fold structures (*minor folds*) that have caused disagreements amongst academic geologists for many years. For this book, we aim to simplify the geology and structure for the interested amateur, and shall not burden the reader with the complexities or the jargon that we might, as structural geologists, use in academic publications. For those unfamiliar with folded rocks, Glossary Figure 1 illustrates, in simplified form, some of the features of the major and minor folds in this area.

The Coastguard Station is built on a prominent rocky outcrop of the hard white *quartzite*, called the Holyhead Quartzite. The Holyhead Quartzite Formation is in the lower part of the Mona Complex succession of Precambrian-Cambrian rocks, sandwiched between the South Stack Formation below and the Rhoscolyn Formation above, which we shall see at other localities. Leeward of the building, the sloping rock face shows downdip *glacial striae* and undulations that reveal its recent past under ice during the Ice Age. This slope, or *dip* of the rocks, indicates the present-day orientation of the sedimentary layering, where it turns at the crest of an *anticline* whose *fold axis plunges* gently towards the NE. It is best to view all the small folds in the Rhoscolyn area looking NE, parallel to the plunge of the fold axes.

From the Coastguard Station, follow the main coastal path SE and go through a swing gate in a wall. Walk diagonally across the field towards the cliffs, where you will notice that the rocks are different: greyer and sandier than the quartzite just seen. These rocks are interbedded gritty sandstones and thinner mudstones of the Rhoscolyn Formation that are generally dipping steeply on the SE *limb* of the Rhoscolyn Anticline (Figure 1b).

Locality 2: around a gully [265749]
A gully just SE of the wall with the swing-gate reveals a 2m-thick

2. Steeply dipping Rhoscolyn Formation mudstone and sandstone beds at locality 2, with prominent quartz veins parallel to the schistosity in the mudstone, showing late folding.

mudstone bed within the sandstones of the Rhoscolyn Formation (Figure 2). The steep southeast dip of the beds is clear, but the rocks are complicated by several features of deformation and metamorphism. The mudstone, metamorphosed into a green schist, contains numerous quartz veins, and close examination shows these to be buckled into folds. These veins that are now folded were crystallised as part of the low grade metamorphism of the mudstone, parallel to a planar schistosity that was developed at the same time. This schistosity is clear in the left sandstone bed in Figure 2, where it is almost perpendicular to the prominent bedding plane at the top-right; the schistosity is more intense and at a closer angle to bedding in the intervening schist/mudstone. Folding of the quartz veins and of the schistosity in the mudstones both indicate that there has been a second episode of deformation and folding, superimposed on the first deformation that created the major Rhoscolyn Anticline and its subsidiary minor folds.

Southeastwards of this gully, the massive sandstones of the Rhoscolyn Formation can be observed in folds on different scales, from both first and second episodes of deformation, making these rocks fascinating to study right down to the smallest scale (Figure 3). These rocks are generally described as *turbidites*, a name given for sediments – usually sandstones and mudstones – that were deposited rapidly on deep continental shelf from the action of turbidity currents. Some of the sandstone beds around this locality and to the southeast reveal sedimentary 'way up', *graded bedding* where pebbly or gritty bases fine upwards to muddier tops. Here, bedding dips steeply to the southeast, and 'way up' evidence shows that the beds get younger to the southeast, supporting their position on this limb of the Rhoscolyn Anticline (Figure 1b).

Now go back to the swing gate in the wall that you first came through and cross to the prominent outcrop wall of Holyhead Quartzite on which the Coastguard Station is sited.

3. Synclinal fold in Rhoscolyn Formation sandstone near locality 2 looking NE, showing steep axial plane cleavage, and crosscutting later folds on the lower-left of the picture.

Locality 3: Holyhead Quartzite [265750]

This locality starts at the prominent steep wall of white quartzite, that here marks the junction of the Holyhead Quartzite with the Rhoscolyn Formation (the latter unseen here but visible in the gully below, and locality 2). The quartzite surface dips at 50° to the SE, showing that the beds are turning over the *axis* of the Rhoscolyn Anticline (Figure 1). If you climb up into the exposures above, you will see that the homogeneous quartzite has *cleavage* planes dipping to the west, but bedding is hard to detect.

4. View of the Rhoscolyn Anticline, looking NE from locality 4, showing minor folds of sandstones and mudstones in the South Stack Formation in the crest of the anticline.

Follow the path back over to the Coastguard Station where you began, noting that you are walking on Holyhead Quartzite exposures. Continue on the main path, in a NW direction, going downslope until the path flattens between two prominent gullies, about 200m from the Coastguard Station. Take a small path to the left around the head of the second gully, and keep left (going south) to follow sheep tracks onto the headland bounded by the two deep, fault-controlled gullies, to reach locality 4 (Figure 1).

Locality 4: headland in the core of the Rhoscolyn Anticline [262751]

Locality 4 is at the southern end of the headland; the grassy slope looks rather steep, but flattens out before you reach the rocks at the coast and is quite safe. From here, looking back at the cliff below the Coastguard Station, you get a superb view of the

Rhoscolyn Anticline (Figure 4). Above to the left is the flat-lying Holyhead Quartzite, which you saw at locality 1. Beneath in the cliffs is a transitional junction into the South Stack Formation, and these are the rocks exposed where you are standing. To the right in the cliffs, towards localities 2 and 3, you can see this junction with the quartzite above, curving down into the steep SE limb of the Rhoscolyn Anticline (Figure 1).

The rocks of the South Stack Formation are interbedded sandstones and mudstones, that after low-grade metamorphism appear schistose, rather similar in appearance to those in the Rhoscolyn Formation seen at locality 2. The rocks at the end of this headland (see foreground of Figure 4) exhibit beautiful *minor folds*, that are in the *hinge* region of the *major fold*, the Rhoscolyn Anticline. Most of the folds are symmetrical waves, and some of the folds have an *axial-plane* cleavage. In detail, some folds appear to be of the first generation, with a cleavage

5. *Deceptively gentle folds in sandstone and mudstone of the South Stack Formation, at locality 5, overfolding to the right (SE). In the foreground are folds descending downwards in quartz veins, that are of a later generation.*

parallel to their axial planes; other folds have a more complicated geometry, with evidence of a second folding deformation indicated by folded cleavage and quartz veins.

Return to the cliff top and walk northwards parallel to gully to the west of this headland. A pair of ravens regularly nest in the gully and choughs are not uncommon. Turn left at the head of the gully, heading southwest over a hillock and grassy slopes towards the right-hand of the two large off-shore islands (Maen-y-fran).

Locality 5: rock ledges facing Maen-y-fran [259752]
Descend carefully to the ledges on the cliff edge, which is ENE from the island. Here you will see flat-bedded thin sandstones and mudstones displaying wonderful small-scale folds that plunge to the NE and are therefore best viewed looking NE (Figure 5). Overall the folds in the sandstones overfold towards the hinge of the Rhoscolyn Anticline (Figure 1), near locality 4 and SE of here. The mudstones contain quartz veins that are

6. *Dewatering structures within the South Stack Formation sandstone at locality 5.*

tightly folded on a small scale, with a different orientation from the folds of sedimentary beds, and are indicative of the second folding phase (see notes on locality 2).

On the cliff top above the ledge, one 20-30cm thick bed exhibits exceptionally clear *de-watering structures* (Figure 6). Seen in two dimensions, these water-escape structures have 'synclinal', rounded but slightly flattened, bases, alternating with 'anticlines' that have pointed crests. They result from the gravitational instability of a sedimentary sequence deposited in deep-water, where the more homogeneous water-laden sediments beneath partly coherent beds attempt to escape upwards. The importance of these structures is that they provide 'way up' evidence, and clearly show that the South Stack Formation is the right-way-up, ie not overturned by folding.

Localities 2-5 demonstrate the downward sedimentary succession of formations on the NE limb of the Rhoscolyn Anticline and across its core within the South Stack Formation, and make up a satisfactory demonstration of this major fold (Figure 1). The next localities take you northwards around the coast, across the Holyhead Quartzite again into the Rhoscolyn Formations of the northwest limb of the Rhoscolyn Anticline. Although access to the rocks on this limb is more limited, it makes a pleasant walk with good views of the rocks and their folds in the cliffs, some spectacular coastal scenery, and many flowers, birds and occasional seals.

From locality 5, ascend the grassy slope northwards and regain the coastal path going westwards. As you approach the coast again you will pass the intriguing and dramatic structure of St. Gwenfaen's well [25957544] believed to be the site of a settlement of a 6th or 7th century hermit saint. Leave the path as you approach the sea and walk WSW down to near the cliff edge.

7. The Holyhead Quartzite overlying the South Stack Formation as seen from the cliff-top at locality 6, looking N.

Locality 6: junction at Porth Gwalch [259754]

At this locality (Figure 1), you are standing on the rocks of the South Stack Formation, but looking N, you will see the Holyhead Quartzite across Porth Gwalch, a W-trending fault gully (Figure 7). The bedding in the quartzite can be seen to be flat-lying on this southwestern limb of the Rhoscolyn Anticline, and the folded sedimentary junction of the South Stack and Holyhead Quartzite Formations is noticeable half-way down the cliff; it is not recommended that a descent be made to examine it!

Return to the path, through the swing gate and on to the Holyhead Quartzite outcrop that forms the prominent Rhoscolyn Head, well known to rock climbers. It is not easy to see the bedding in this rather homogeneous quartzite, but it is approximately parallel to the outcrop surface below the wall. A more prominent feature in these rocks is the steep-dipping, ENE-trending cleavage. As you walk around the cliff top you will see a gradual change in the composition of the blocks in the wall, from the white colour of the Holyhead Quartzite into the greyer colour of the Rhoscolyn Formation sandstones. On the ground, and in contrast to the southeastern limb seen at locality 3, the sedimentary junction of the Holyhead Quartzite and Rhoscolyn Formation is transitional and difficult to pinpoint, here. Other indications that you have walked across the junction (at about 258756) into the overlying Rhoscolyn Formation is that these greyer quartzites contain white quartz veins, and glimpses of exposures in the cliffs reveal upright folds of bedding with steep NW-dipping axial plane cleavage.

Continue to walk along the coastal path northeastwards, crossing a prominent *fault* gully that in some tidal conditions creates a blow-hole in the field at [259757], that is concealed behind a high

8. View NE towards Porth Saint. In the foreground, the Rhoscolyn Formation beds dip NW, crossed by steeper NW-dipping cleavage.

stone wall. Beyond a hand-rail, walk a little way down the grassy slope to view a cliff face [260758] with well-marked beds of Rhoscolyn Formation sandstone and mudstone, dipping NW with small folds overfolding to the SE, crossed by steeply-dipping cleavage (Figure 8). These structures confirm our position on the NW limb of the Rhoscolyn Anticline (Figure 1b). Beyond, shown in the backgound to Figure 8, you will see that the back wall of Porth Saint bay is a vivid red colour. This marks the position of a WNW-trending fault, that has been the locus of iron-saturated fluids. You will also gain a good view of the Porth Saint Syncline that we shall examine at the next locality.

Continue to walk around the coastal path northwards. At the southeastern end of Porth Saint, just beyond a footbridge, note that there is a swing-gate marking the beginning of a footpath that leads back to Rhoscolyn Church. You will return this way, at the end of this excursion.

Locality 7: Porth Saint syncline [259759]

To the west of Porth Saint bay, we have seen that the peninsula clearly displays a large-scale, upright, open *syncline* (Figure 9; also Figure 1), in a quartzite within the Rhoscolyn Formation. It

9. *Syncline in quartzite within the Rhoscolyn Formation on the cliffs to the west of Porth Saint at locality 7, looking NE.*

65

is worth leaving the main path and walking around the coast, where you can access the steep NW-dipping quartzites on the SE limb of this syncline at its southern end. If you regain the cliff top you can also access the syncline at its NW end. Here bedding around the open syncline is clearly marked by a basin-like ledge, where a distinct mudstone bed underlies the massive quartzite with its pronounced subvertical cleavage.

Keeping near the cliff top as you walk towards the next locality, you can see large-scale folds in the cliffs, marked by sandstone beds overfolding to the southeast, again indicative of the fold geometry on this limb of the Rhoscolyn Anticline (Figure 1b).

Locality 8: Natural Arch [259762]
A natural arch marks the southern side of Bwa Gwyn, and is one of the most spectacular features of coastal erosion at Rhoscolyn. In sunshine, the Rhoscolyn Formation here appears as a dazzling

10. Natural arch, locality 8, as seen looking west. The cave at the bottom right of the photograph has a large flute cast.

white quartzite (sandstone) that is full of fractures (faults and joints), including the bridge to the arch (Figure 10). The main fault that controls this arch is a continuation of the fault at the back of Porth Saint (Figure 1). If you view the arch from the south, across the gully, as pictured in Figure 9 (right side), you can see a small cave with the base of a quartzite marking its roof. The quartzite is corrugated by the most dramatic bulbous *flute-cast*, a sedimentary erosional feature caused by high-energy sea-floor currents. On the basis of the geometry of the large and small flute-casts, experts who have descended to the cave suggest that the sedimentary currents came from the northeast.

Continue to walk near the coast, northwards, for 250m, until you spot a prominent bay, and an obvious change of rocks to the north: this is Bwa Du, the final locality (Figure 1).

11. The folds of yellow and white sandstone at Bwa Du, locality 9, overfolding to the SE. In the background, across the Bwa Du Fault, is the darker New Harbour Formation with its horizontal schistosity.

Locality 9: Bwa Du fold and fault [261763]

To the south of the gully called Bwa Du, there is a peninsula that provides a good view northwards of a spectacular fold-pair in quartzite and sandstone beds within the Rhoscolyn Formation (Figure 11). The folds have an axial-planar cleavage and clear overfolding towards the southeast, confirming a position on the NW limb of the Rhoscolyn Anticline (Figure 1b). The yellow-coloured sandstone in the syncline is crossed by a later shallow NW-dipping cleavage that indicates the second deformation, seen elsewhere at Rhoscolyn.

The Bwa Du Fault, which is here the southeast expression of the North Stack Fault, provides a rare opportunity to examine one of the best-exposed faults on Anglesey. It is expressed as a 15m-wide gully (Figure 12) between the ruggedly exposed yellowish

12. View looking west, of the Bwa Du fault gully. On the left are the sandstones of the Rhoscolyn Formation. On the right and in the coastal crags are the dark grey-green schists of the New Harbour Formation. Holyhead Mountain appears in the far distance.

quartzite of the Rhoscolyn Formation to its SE, and the lower-lying cliffs of the green-grey *schists* of the New Harbour Formation to its NW. The fault zone is about 14m wide, trends ESE with a near-vertical orientation, and is marked by a fault breccia comprised of angular fragments of quartzite in a schistose matrix. The Rhoscolyn Formation sandstones on the southwest side of the fault zone gully dips steeply north, and folds and cleavage are clearly seen, as noted above. The rocks of the New Harbour Formation on the northeast side of the fault form the dark grey background of Figure 11. These rocks have a flat-lying *schistosity* that gives a finely layered appearance to the rocks, and on close examination you may see small folds that have a different geometry from the more obvious larger folds that overfold SE.

The New Harbour Formation forms almost continuous coastal outcrops from this locality northwards for 4 km. We describe it at the locality of Porth y Pwll, on the north shore of Treaddur Bay; and in the excursion following this one, to Rhoscolyn Bay, where its boundary with the underlying Rhoscolyn Formation is a natural sedimentary junction. Rejoin the main coastal footpath and head southwards back to Porth Saint (locality 7), and take the marked footpath inland from here that that leads directly back to Rhoscolyn Church.

G. Rhoscolyn Bay

The coastline centred on Rhoscolyn has a lovely bay and sandy beach that is popular both with families, and for boating and canoeing. There is a beach car park with seasonal public conveniences, and an attractive inn nearby, but the narrow winding lane leading to the beach can sometimes become congested in summer. This locality is part of the Rhoscolyn coastal area that featured in the preceding Rhoscolyn Headlands excursion. We have separated Rhoscolyn Bay into a stand-alone trip to two localities, based on parking at the beach car park (Figure 1). It is possible to include these localities with the preceding Rhoscolyn Headlands trip, by parking at Rhoscolyn Church, but that involves a longer and more circuitous walking route, and requires a change in order of localities.

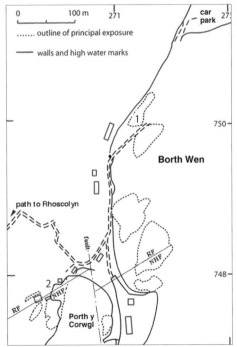

We recommend that you make the Rhoscolyn Headlands excursion first, where you can walk across the Rhoscolyn Anticline in Mona complex rocks, and end by seeing the New Harbour Formation in faulted contact with the Rhoscolyn Formation. This Rhoscolyn Bay excursion allows you to make a close inspection of the boundary

1. Map of Rhoscolyn Bay area showing locality 1 at Borthwen (Rhoscolyn Beach) and locality 2 at Porth y Corwygl.

between these two formations, where it is a normal sedimentary contact exposed on the shore, arguably the best place on Holy Island to examine this boundary. The rocks here complete the cross-sectional picture of the Rhoscolyn Anticline built up on the Rhoscolyn Headlands excursion (its Figure 1); here we are on the steep-dipping SE fold *limb* of the *major anticline*. A low to mid tide is recommended, to enable easiest access to a second bay.

From the Britannia Bridge take the A55 about 25km to exit 3, signposted Valley. If coming from Rhosneigr, rejoin the A55 in the Holyhead direction, and you will reach exit 3 after about 13km. Follow the A5 from the A55 roundabout to Valley (1km) where there are shops and cafes. At the traffic lights, turn left on to the B4545, signposted Trearddur Bay. After nearly 2km, you will cross the Four-Mile Bridge on to Holy Island; immediately after the bridge, fork left on to a minor road signposted Rhoscolyn. In 4km you will come to the prominent church of St. Gwenfaen, that is the recommended parking place for the Rhoscolyn headlands excursion. On approaching Rhoscolyn Church, follow the lane left, signposted to The White Eagle (inn) and Beach, and drive down the narrow winding lane 2 km, to reach the free beach car park at the end. An alternative is to leave the car at the church, and access this additional excursion on foot, by the coastal path or lane.

From the Rhoscolyn Beach car park (Figure 1), walk directly on to the beach, and head right (south), close to the sea wall, across the sand onto the beach outcrops.

Locality 1: Rhoscolyn Beach/Borthwen [272750]
The rocks here are dominantly sandstones in the upper part of the Rhoscolyn Formation (Figure 2), exposed as far as a stream emerging from a portal in the wall. Bedding dips steeply SE, and a first generation *cleavage* that is visible in the muddier sediments dips more steeply NW. Sedimentary evidence is quite hard to find, but rare *cross-bedding* and grading show that the

2. The shore rocks of Rhoscolyn Formation sandstones at Borthwen (locality 1), viewed SW from Rhoscolyn Beach.

3. Close up of a conglomerate lens in the Rhoscolyn Formation at locality 1.

beds are right-way up, getting younger to the southeast. Together, these relationships are compatible with the outcrops being on the steep SE limb of the major Rhoscolyn Anticline: see Rhoscolyn Headlands excursion, Figure 1, and Glossary Figure 1.

Within the sandstones, but sometimes hidden under seaweed, there are lenses up to 5m long and a metre or so wide of *conglomerate* (Figure 3). Surfaces of the rock reveal mainly elliptical-shaped clasts with diameters from 1 to 20 cm long, and *clast* compositions ranging from sandstone to siltstone, similar to the lithologies seen in the Rhoscolyn Formation nearby. The conglomerate persists in two discontinuous beds for many tens of metres, including exposures at the base of the walls below houses. These lenses of conglomerate are consistent with channel deposition within turbidite sedimentation.

4. *Looking SW at the junction between the folded Rhoscolyn Formation sandstones in the cliff, and the New Harbour Formation schists and black tuff beneath, at Porth y Corwygl (locality 2).*

Continue around the bay to the last outcrop of the Rhoscolyn Formation before the wall. Now go up to the path leading towards a gate to some white houses and down to the next bay called Porth y Corwygl (Figure 1). Walk to the right to the prominent cliffs with trailing rock plants below a house, on the northwest side of the bay.

Locality 2: Porth y Corwygl [270747]

In these cliffs we see the junction of the Rhoscolyn Formation with the New Harbour Formation to its southeast (Figure 4), and examine its nature by comparing the rocks and minor structures on its two sides. We define the junction as the sharp change at the base of the cliff, where the rocks change from the steep sandstone beds that make up the cliff, into black schistose rock for several metres SE-wards, before it has the appearance of more typical New Harbour Formation *schists*. We can see no evidence that this is a strongly deformed or faulted junction, as has been suggested

5. The same junction as in Figure 4, but looking NE, showing the pock-marked New Harbour Formation tuff on the left, and folds in the schists to the right.

by some geologists. The black rock near the base of the New Harbour Formation (Figure 4) was described as a volcanic *tuff* in the first Geological Survey of Anglesey in 1919. Its primary composition and texture are not obvious in the field evidence because of the low-grade *metamorphism* that has affected all the rocks at Rhoscolyn. The tuff is a finely laminated rock with a locally pock-marked appearance (Figure 5) caused by the weathering out of pinkish carbonate mineral clots.

In the sandstones of the Rhoscolyn Formation, seen in the cliffs of Figure 4, *folds* with a low *plunge* to the NE are seen. These fold the main *schistosity* as well as bedding, showing that these are a later fold generation. They have a similar style to folds seen in the New Harbour Formation immediately above stratigraphically, that are shown in Figure 5. Here, the New Harbour Formation is somewhat darker than the typical silver-green schists seen further above the junction. More typical exposures of the New Harbour Formation schist are seen by walking around the bay of Porth y Corwygl, eastwards [271747], where the rock is a schistose mudstone that contains fine sedimentary laminations characteristic of laminated *turbidites* that were deposited in deep water. The dominant schistosity that is parallel to this lamination is marked by the alignement of fine-grained *quartz*, *chlorite* and *muscovite*, producing a *mineral lineation* on the fine layer surfaces.

The New Harbour Formation forms extensive coastal exposures around the coast of Holy Island and across to mainland Anglesey. It mantles the Rhoscolyn Anticline, as shown on the Rhoscolyn Headlands excursion, and dominates the coastline in the region of Treaddur Bay and beyond. We recommend the Porth y Pwll excursion as the best place to study the structures in these rocks.

Return from here across the neck of land to Rhoscolyn Beach (Borthwen), and back to the car park.

H. Treaddur Bay

This is possibly the most popular beach on Anglesey, with its broad shallow sandy bay, bordered by schists of the New Harbour Formation on its two sides (Figure 1). The rocks are best seen at the south side of the beach and best examined at medium to low tide. From the Britannia Bridge continue on the A55 across Anglesey northwards and take the number 5 exit, signposted Valley; at the Valley traffic lights turn left on to Holy Island and keep on the B4545 for 4km to Treaddur Bay, where there is a pay and display car park [256790] with toilets. Walk south around the beach or road (at high tide) to the south to the first outcrops of the grey-black shiny schistose rocks. Note the boulders of *gabbro* and *serpentinite* used for beach-head defence on the way, seen at the left margin of Figure 1, assumed to be from intrusions of basic and ultrabasic igneous rocks into the New Harbour Formation a few km inland from here. The first exposures beyond

1. View of part of Treaddur Bay looking SW, with the beach-head boulders in the foreground and the exposures discussed, beyond.

the boulders are rather seaweed-covered, but, if you continue to the bay just before a slipway from a boat-house, there are some cleaner exposures in the cliff, discussed below (Figure 2).

2. Minor folds of the layering in the bay near the boat-house, looking NE.

The rocks, similar to those that you can better examine at the Porth y Pwll site, consist of finely-layered (mm-scale) *schists* made up from *chlorite, muscovite, quartz* and *feldspar* in a variety of combinations. Bedding is part of this layering as you can see from the subtle changes in the concentrations of these minerals, so that darker micaceous laminae alternate with the paler ones richer in quartz, that were originally thin beds of mudstones and siltstones. The earliest deformation, from the evidence here, produced a fine layering or schistosity apparently parallel to bedding. Thin quartz veins parallel to the layering, as well as the layers themselves, show a 'stretching' of quartz grains on their surfaces producing a marked *lineation*. This stretching indicates the direction that the rocks were extended at the time when they were first deformed. You may be able to find tight *folds*, which fold the layering and the lineation and overfold to the SE (Figure 2). A later set of quartz veins, probably injected along a steep-dipping joint set, cuts across these folds. These features are typical of this rock formation everywhere it is exposed on this coast and so well-seen in this and the Porth y Pwll section.

I. Porth y Pwll

This locality is one of the most accessible and pleasant for a detailed examination of the typical lithologies and structural style of the New Harbour Formation. The localities described are generally accessible at all except high tides; be wary of slippery boulders. The pebbles on the beach here exhibit many of the features described below.

Follow directions from the Britannia Bridge as described for the Treaddur Bay excursion and then, travelling north through the village, take a left turn for South Stack (only signposted with a brown sign at time of writing) opposite the boatyard [255793]. In 1km the road bends sharply left by the entrance to the large hotel signed as Plas Darian, and then comes back near the coast,

1. The beach at Porth y Pwll, looking south. The steps to the beach are at the bottom left of the photo and locality 1 is in the cliff beneath the photographer; locality 2 is in the low-lying reefs just visible beyond the figures on the beach and locality 3 is at the far right-hand end of the cliff.

opposite two houses. There is good parking by the second of two new stone sea-walls, opposite a minor road labelled Traeth Atsain. From the coastal promontory here there is a good view of the bay called Porth y Pwll that we will explore (Figure 1). Now walk back on a coastal path towards the first wall, before which a flight of steps (often hidden by vegetation) leads down to the beach [244793], as shown on the map (Figure 2).

Locality 1
Turn right on the beach and within a few metres you will see a low cliff section on your right, exhibiting typical features of the New Harbour Formation. The rocks consist of finely-layered (mm-scale) *schists* made up from *chlorite, muscovite, quartz* and *feldspar* in a variety of combinations. Bedding is apparently parallel to this *schistosity* and is seen as subtle changes in the concentrations of these minerals, so that more or less micaceous beds alternate with those richer in quartz and feldspar preserving

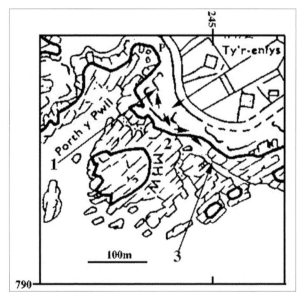

2. The Map of the area SE of Porth y Pwll showing position of localities 1, 2 and 3. P = parking, arrow-heads indicate route between road and localities.

the original fine sedimentary layering in a laminated mud and silt. Bed thickness varies from mms to tens of cms. Look out for rare thin (mm to cm) distinctly 'gritty' beds with grains of quartz and feldspar about one mm in diameter, in this otherwise rather monotonous lithology.

The composite bedding/schistosity on the flat limbs of the large *folds dips* very gently (up to 10°) to the north or northwest, but the dominant feature is the cascade of *minor folds* with *axes* that *plunge* gently northeast (Figure 3), perhaps the most attractive example anywhere of this feature. The folds descend to the southeast at an angle of about 20° and have a wavelength varying from a few cms to tens of cms and an amplitude of a similar range. Their most noticeable feature is their asymmetry, with alternating long 'flat' limbs and short steep (vertical to

3. New Harbour Formation at locality 1, illustrating the mm-scale bedding and schistosity and the scale of the main folding overfolding to the SE. The pencil is parallel to the axial-planes of the folds and the later crenulation cleavage. One earlier fold closure, marked by a quartz vein, can be seen about 5cm above the pencil point; view looking NE.

overturned) limbs. The *axial-planes* of the folds typically dip about 30-40° to the northwest and are marked in the more schistose beds by a *crenulation cleavage.*

Quartz veins, commonly a few mms to a cm or more in thickness are seen to be sub-parallel to the schistosity. Other quartz veins, clearly later, are steeper and cut across both the schistosity and the folds. A noticeable feature on the exposed schistosity surfaces particularly evident on the flat limbs of the folds, also seen on the thin parallel quartz veins, is a marked *lineation* of the quartz minerals, often called a *stretching lineation*, that is the direction in which the minerals were made to extend while the schistosity was being generated. On careful observation it will be seen that the steep limbs of some folds preserve an earlier generation of tight to *isoclinal folds*, clearly refolded by the main set described above (see description of Figure 3).

This is a superb section in which to summarise the history of the deformation of the New Harbour Formation, although the precise sequence of events is a matter of considerable debate. The earliest event, from the evidence here, was the production of a schistosity apparently parallel to bedding, with the production of the thin quartz veins and the 'stretching' of mineral grains on their surfaces. The tight to isoclinal folds, mentioned above and seen in Figures 4 and 5, may have formed at the same time as this schistosity. The latter are folded by the main set of minor and major folds overfolding to the SE, typical of this rock formation everywhere it is exposed on this coast and so well-seen in this section with its associated crenulation cleavage. A later set of quartz veins, probably injected along a steep-dipping joint set, cuts across both the schistosity and these folds.

Locality 2
Southeast of the steps and the outcrop described above, there is a 50m long area of low outcrop, usually accessible, but high tide should be avoided. The overfolding to the SE of the minor folds

4. *Folds in the New Harbour Formation on beach reefs at locality 2.*
a) The main folds refold an earlier fold-pair, below the pencil and
enlarged in (b).
b) Detail of the early folds whose NE-trending axes are approximately
parallel to the pencil. Bedding is shown by the darker, thin, mud-rich
beds and the gritty bed below the pencil.

5. The large-scale late fold in the New Harbour Formation in the cliffs at locality 3; note minor folds in the steep limb and the crenulation cleavage in centre of steep limb. View to the NE; cliff is about 6m high.

described above, are exceptionally well-seen here. On close scrutiny you will see that there are many examples of refolded earlier isoclinal folds, 2-3 cm in amplitude. It is difficult to measure the axial trends of this earlier set, but there is one clearly-exposed fold-pair (Figure 4a & b) about 8cm in amplitude, of the earlier isoclines with a penetrative axial-planar schistosity.

Locality 3 [245792]

The previous section ends abruptly to the southeast in a 10m high cliff. If the tide is not too high and taking great care over boulders that can be very slippery, you can make a traverse of about 15m at the foot of this cliff. This leads to a superb example of one of the large-scale latest folds that characterise the New Harbour Formation (Figure 5). It is necessary to stand back from the cliff to appreciate the geometry of this fold that has a steep, slightly overturned, limb some 8m high. In close-up, it can be seen that smaller-scale folds, of bedding and parallel quartz veins, corrugate this shorter, steeper, limb. A well-developed axial-planar crenulation cleavage affects the dark schist, formerly mudstone, that has been thickened in fold cores. It is interesting to note that these features – the small-scale folds and the thickened mudstone beds – are scarcely seen on the flat limbs of the major fold, suggesting perhaps that these limbs have been stretched, and bedding thinned, whereas the steep limbs have thickened. Large-scale folds of this later generation, overfolding towards the southeast, are generally a feature of the New Harbour Formation everywhere on Holy Island from Holyhead as far southeast as Rhoscolyn, where they have had a significant effect in modifying the geometry of the first generation Rhoscolyn Anticline.

J. Porth y Post

Porth y Post is an attractive sandy bay with rock pools (Figure 1), to the west of Treaddur Bay and about 300m northwest of Porth y Pwll where the New Harbour Formation is seen at its best. Those walking the coastal path in this area could easily combine these two nearby excursions. Porth y Post provides another opportunity to look at structures in the New Harbour Formation, but the main reason for its inclusion is the exceptionally clear exposure of a swarm of Cenozoic *dolerite dykes* at the south of the bay.

1. Porth y Post beach looking NW. The New Harbour Formation schists occupy the foreground and background, and the dolerite dykes occupy the foreshore to the right of the central stack, whose dark base is a side view of one dyke dipping away from the viewer.

From the Britannia Bridge continue on the A55 across Anglesey northwards and take the number 5 exit, signposted Valley; at the Valley traffic lights turn left on to Holy Island and keep on the B4545 for 4km to Treaddur Bay. Travelling north through the village of Treaddur Bay, take a left turn opposite the boatyard [255793] that has a brown horse-shoe sign to Porth y Post stables. This junction also has a brown sign for South Stack. Following this coastal road, in about 2km you pass the riding stables on your right, and straight afterwards arrive at the small bay of Porth y Post (Figure 1). There is limited parking on the right of the road [243794]. Medium to low tides are best, in order to appreciate the intertidal beach exposures of dykes.

The cliffs in the New Harbour Formation *schists*, are well-exposed on both sides of the bay and are easily accessible both on the beach and from the coastal paths. The rocks, similar to those

2. The small headland on the south side of Porth y Post that contains about seven dolerite dykes with moderate to steep dips northwards. Looking NE.

3. *One of the dolerite dykes in the centre of Figure 2, showing off-shoots into the flat-lying New Harbour Schists. Spheroidal weathering is seen on the beach exposure. Detail of the left dyke margin is shown in Figure 4.*

that you can also examine in the Porth y Pwll or Treaddur Bay excursions, consist of finely-layered (mm-scale) schists made up from chlorite, muscovite, quartz and feldspar in a variety of combinations. Bedding, seen as subtle changes in the concentrations of these minerals, is parallel to this *schistosity* and has thickness varying from mms to tens of cms, so that more or less micaceous beds alternate with those richer in quartz and feldspar. Looking carefully at the quartz-rich beds, you might be able to persuade yourself that they grade into the more mica-rich seams. Look out for rare thin (mm to cm) distinctly 'gritty' beds with grains of quartz and feldspar about one mm in diameter.

The structural features that are particularly well seen here are the tight-to-*isoclinal folds*, that are apparently the earliest to be developed, and that are folded by the main set of *minor* and *major* folds overfolding to the SE. These features are well seen on the second peninsular in the low cliff on the beach, just inside its south side [243793]. But of particular interest here is the swarm of steep-dipping, half to one metre-wide, dolerite dykes that cut across the near-horizontal schists in this area of the cliffs (Figure 2), and can be traced WNW across the beach to the sea stack that is underlain by one of the dykes (Figure 1). At least seven dykes can be seen across the cliff section of Figure 2, some showing very clear spheroidal weathering. One of the prominent dykes in this cliff section (Figure 3), cuts across – making it later than – unusually tight folds of the main set in the adjacent schists. What is particularly clear here is that these folds can be seen to refold earlier, tightly packed, cm-scale isoclinal folds, as seen in detail in Figure 4.

4. Detail of the right-hand side of the dyke shown in Figure 3. The schists exhibit tight folds of the main generation that refold earlier small-scale isoclinal folds, best seen near the coin. View NE.

The rocks exposed on the shore between the cliff section and the sea stack at low to medium tide (Figure 1) provide some remarkably clear views of dolerite dykes and dykelets with interesting off-shoots and branches, some of which are seen in Figure 5. Here also, some dykes show fine-grained cooling at their margins with coarser-grained, *vesicle*-rich interiors, and many show *spheroidal weathering*. These dykes at Porth y Post, and similar ones seen intruding different rocks at Porth Dafarch, are part of the Cenozoic dyke swarm of Great Britain, associated with opening of the North Atlantic 40-60 million years ago.

5. *Dolerite dykes exposed in plan on the foreshore, showing off-shoots and spiky terminations with chilled margins.*

K. Porth Dafarch

This must be one of the most pleasant beaches on Anglesey, only about 3km from Holyhead that has an abundance of hotels, shops, restaurants and daily ferries to Ireland. It was once used as a port for packet boats to Ireland when the port at Holyhead was unavailable. It has 'seasonal' toilets and visiting ice cream and snack vans and is very busy in the summer and at fine weekends. You can park on the road by the sea wall or, if the beach is not too busy you may be able to park below the wall or on a section of the old road to the left of the junction.

From the Britannia Bridge, keep on the A55 to the first roundabout on the outskirts of Holyhead. Here turn sharp left on

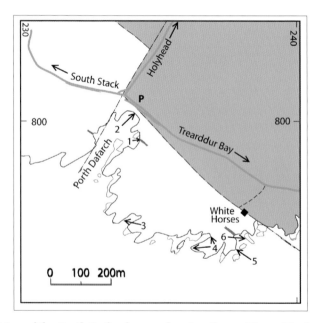

1. Map of the Porth Dafarch area showing the position of the localities described in the text. The coloured area is the New Harbour Formation, separated from the South Stack Formation (blank) by the North Stack Fault.

the B4545, but turn immediately right by the Foresters Arms on to a minor road, signposted Porth Dafarch Road on the side of the pub, and in about 2km you will come to the junction with the coastal road at Porth Dafarch (Figure 1) [233799]. If you are coming from the Porth y Pwll locality keep on the narrow coastal road, travelling west, until you come to this junction after about one and a half kilometres.

2. View of Porth Dafarch beach from the south; the fold shown in Figure 3 is at the back of the left of the beach; the dyke shown in Figure 4 is in the low cliff nearest to the camera.

Go down onto the beach that is accessible except at the very highest tide (Figure 2) and turn right, across a stream to the first exposures. Here (Figure 3) well-exposed folds in the South Stack Group sandstones and siltstones are seen below the sea wall. If you look particularly at the thin beds of delicately-striped siltstones, you will find SE-younging *cross-laminations*, demonstrating that the long *limbs* of the *folds* are overturned. These folds relate to the overturned limb of a *major anticline* that dominates this coastline for several kms to the north and south. The folds display a well-developed *axial-planar schistosity* and this, you may be able to see, locally is overprinted by a later *cleavage* which dips to the NW. This second deformation here has very little effect, producing only small-scale folds and this localised cleavage, but elsewhere (see Rhoscolyn excursion) can be responsible for large-scale folding and a penetrative cleavage.

Now cross back to the south side of the beach. After passing more exposures of South Stack Group sandstones and mudstones, showing some more small-scale folds, plunging steeply NE, you will come to a depression in the low cliff on the southeast side of the bay that contains heavily weathered exposures of a *dolerite*

3. The fold-pair seen near the centre of the beach.

4. The heavily weathered NW-trending dolerite dyke.

dyke [234799] (Figure 4). The less weathered part of the exposure shows a coarse *gabbroic* texture of the pink *feldspar* and dark *pyroxene*; in thin-section these dykes of Tertiary age (about 50 million years) are seen to be *olivine*-bearing. Anglesey is crossed by a swarm of these NW-SE trending dykes, which usually make upstanding features in the landscape. This dyke is about 16m wide and trends 140° towards the far northwest side of the sandy bay; its continuation can be seen by the electricity substation, where it is about 20m wide. However, it has been displaced to the left (in a left-lateral sense) by about 100m (Figure 1) by a *fault* that runs up the valley to the NE of the beach.

The subsequent localities described here are at the far end of the cliff to the south and can be accessed by taking the cliff path that starts from the south end of the promenade at the back of the beach. This involves a pleasant 15 minute walk along one of a variety of cliff-top paths, but stay as close you can to the cliff-top

5. Syncline seen from the cliff top at [235796] looking NW.

6. A main set anticline on the cliff top at [237795] with axial-planar cleavage looking NW.

96

to see the variety of geology in the cliff below as well as in exposures on the path. Near the southern end of the cliff top [236796], you get some excellent views of some of the main set folds (Figures 5). The folds show the distortion of the early folds by the later set and the sandstone beds exhibit loaded bases.

At the very end of the cliff-top, if you turn seawards along a narrow peninsula, you can exam one of the main set folds at first-hand (Figure 6), an anticline with a well-developed axial-planar cleavage. Looking back into a cave you will see that another view of that same anticline here with an intense cleavage at its base, suggesting that this is a *thrust*. If you venture down to the ledges to the south of the peninsula you will find many other folds and if you look carefully at some of the thin beds of striped mudstones you may find cross-laminations as those seen in Figure 7, which show that the beds are mostly inverted.

7. Cross-laminations in the finely bedded siltstones in the cliff-top at [234797].

By turning south along the grassy edge of the next gully, there is a fine view (Figure 8) of a 20m-wide dolerite dyke in the gully below; this is a continuation of the heavily-weathered NW-trending olivine-dolerite dyke that we have seen at Porth Dafarch. In the further bay beyond that of the dyke (see Figure 8), the cliff at its back marks the position of the major NW-trending North Stack Fault, separating the rocks of the South Stack Formation that we have been examining from the schists of the New Harbour Formation on the far side, that are seen on the Porth y Pwll excursion. This fault, that we have seen at Rhoscolyn, runs the whole length of Holy Island.

8. *Looking NE at the 20m-wide dolerite dyke at [238796] in the foreground; at the back of the bay are the rocks of the New Harbour Formation.*

L. South Stack

This excursion is concerned with the South Stack Formation, especially its spectacular *folding* seen in these coastal cliffs and the adjacent lighthouse island. The island and the cliffs 6km west of Holyhead, are an RSPB reserve and a popular destination for birdwatchers. There is a visitor centre, shop and café with associated car parking. The lighthouse is of particular interest being built by Trinity House in 1809. An iron suspension bridge was built to replace a rope bridge in 1828 but replaced by the present aluminium structure in 1964. In 1984 the keeper was withdrawn, the lighthouse automated and it is now monitored and controlled by computer from Harwich.

1. South Stack lighthouse looking west from the road above. The anticline/syncline fold-pair described is seen in the gully immediately below the lighthouse; the steep limb of the syncline on the gully wall is corrugated by minor folds overfolding upwards, towards the northwest.

The rocks of the South Stack Formation are alternating sandstone and mudstone at the base of the local sequence of the Mona Complex. You may have seen these rocks on the Rhoscolyn excursion, where they are seen immediately below, and in contact with, the Holyhead Quartzite Formation, whereas here they are about 150m below it. The exposures here are at the lowest structural level seen in the Mona Complex on Holy Island although there is some debate as to whether they are the oldest formation. No body fossils have been found in these rocks, although worm casts are present, that are of latest Precambrian or of earliest Cambrian age. A *radiometric date* of 522 million years has been obtained from small zircon crystals in these rocks, showing that the depositional age of the South Stack Formation at South Stack is early in the Cambrian.

From the Britannia Bridge, keep on the A55 northwards to the first roundabout on the outskirts of Holyhead. Continue through the town, left along the coast road, then take a left at the brown sign to South Stack and RSPB. After about 4km, as you approach the coast, you will see a junction on your right signposted to South Stack. After about 500m there is the large free car park on your left at [211818]. If you are going to visit the South Stack lighthouse (see later), you have to obtain tickets (£4 at time of writing) at the kiosk here.

Walk to the end of the road, and you will soon see spectacular large-scale folding by looking towards the cliff-face beneath the lighthouse on the island (Figure 1). An *anticline* is obvious but a tight syncline to its northeast (right), beneath the lighthouse, less so. The steep right-hand *limb* of the *syncline* is corrugated by a beautiful cascade of *minor folds* of the thinner beds of sandstone overfolding towards the northwest. The folding is a result of the lateral NW-SE compression of the original horizontal sedimentary layers in the *Caledonian Orogeny*, formed at the same time as the Rhoscolyn Anticline (see Rhoscolyn excursion). During this deformation, the original sediments of sandstones and mudstones have been turned into *quartzites* and *schists*.

2. *The main cliff as seen through the "window" in the wall of the steps; the cliff section, looking NE, is some 20m high. We are looking here, to the left, at the overall horizontal beds in the crest of a major anticline; to the right is a fault, beyond which the beds descend steeply to the SE. The small-scale load structures, emphasised by folding, can be seen at the bases of some of the sandstone beds, crossed by the vertical cleavage planes.*

Begin to descend the 400 steps towards the lighthouse until you get the first view to your left, back towards the cliff, of magnificent major folds. Continue further down, noting the upright cleavage that penetrates these rocks, in exposures by the steps, until you come to the 'window' in the left-hand wall of the path looking back at the main cliff face (Figure 2). This is a favourite viewpoint for bird watchers in the nesting season when seagulls, fulmars, guillemots and razorbills crowd the bedding planes that are nearly horizonal in the cliff-face, around the hinges of upright folds. Even from this distance you can see that some sandstone beds exhibit *graded bedding* up into the overlying mudstones; this grading, from coarse grits to fine silts, can be seen at close quarters in the exposures around the 'window'. The bases of the sandstone beds seen in the cliff exhibit small-scale irregularities, *load-structures* resulting from the weight of the massive sandstones into the muds below. *Axial-planar cleavage* in the sandstones is near vertical, resulting from horizontal compression of these sediments, whilst in the weaker muddy beds the cleavage is itself strongly folded by a later episode of deformation resulting from compression that was nearly vertical. This produces smaller-scale folds with axial-planes and associated *crenulation cleavage* dipping at a low angle to the NW. Quartz veins, injected during metamorphism parallel to the earlier cleavage, exhibit this later folding particularly well. A *fault*, sub-parallel to the cleavage, is well-seen to the right in Figure 2.

Continue down to the bottom of the stone and metal steps. Look at the cliff face to your right that is part of the steep SE-dipping limb of a major anticline. The axial-planar cleavage, once vertical, is seen here to be affected by the later folding and cleavage. This is seen particularly well at the foot of the steps in the exposures to your left (Figure 3) where the crenulation cleavage is well

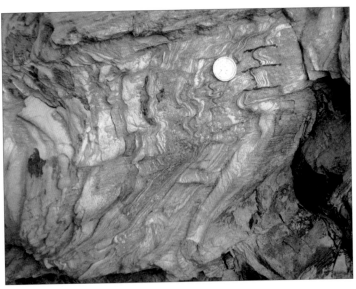

3. Detail of the later folds as seen near the bottom of the steps.
The axial-planar crenulation cleavage related to these folds
(unfortunately overdrawn by someone in felt-tip pen) dips gently NW;
the coin is 25mm across.

developed. Folded quartz veins can also be seen here, of the same later fold generation.

If you have bought tickets, cross to the island and looking back at the cliffs you will get excellent views of the full majesty of the major folds, as well as accompanying minor folds (Figure 4). The mudstones between the sandstones show the development of the later cleavage as well as minor folds affecting the quartz veins. Two faults, one in the centre, the other on the left can also be seen in Figure 4.

4. The major early folds viewed looking NE from South Stack island; note the asymmetry of the minor folds and the development of axial-planar cleavage in the sandstones, the NW-dipping later cleavage in the intervening mudstones and the minor folding of the quartz veins. Two faults can also be seen.

M. Holyhead Country Park

Holyhead Breakwater Country Park has developed into an attractive and popular place for local families and visitors. There is a visitor centre that provides information on the adjacent coastal path and wildlife, exhibitions relating to former industrial activities, a café and toilets, and pay-and-display parking. The geological interest is the opportunity to see both the Holyhead Quartzite Formation – a rock of unusual purity – and the sandstones and mudstones of the younger Rhoscolyn Formation. The formation below the Holyhead Quartzite, the South Stack Formation (see South Stack description), has been dated as 522 million years, which is in the lower part of the Cambrian Period. There are also views here of one of the major faults that affect the rocks of Holy Island.

1. View of the brickworks chimney at Holyhead Breakwater Country Park, with the Holyhead Quartzite in the background. The clear vertical traces are the cleavage; bedding can be seen, as the sub- horizontal break half-way up the rock face. View south.

The *quartzite* was used to build the breakwater that you have passed at Holyhead harbour, the road in fact being the path of the old railway that supplied the material. Later, the rock was used for brickmaking (Figure 1), and supplied much raw material for domestic and industrial use on Anglesey. This quartzite is a startlingly white rock that is almost pure quartz, originally near-pure sandstone that has been metamorphosed; it forms the major landmark of Holyhead Mountain visible over much of Anglesey. The Rhoscolyn Formation, that mainly comprises impure sandstones interbedded with lesser mudstones, forms the low-lying country to the east of the Visitor Centre and is well-exposed on the coast between here and the breakwater to the east.

From the Britannia Bridge continue on the A55 across Anglesey into Holyhead. Continue through the town, following directions to the Breakwater Country Park, turning from the coast road left into the country park. This narrow road is lined by cuttings in the New Harbour Formation *schists* (the old railway track), for nearly 2 km to the buildings and visitor centre at the end of the road [225836], where you can park. If you stop and park partway along the road, by the large warehouse [236836], you can walk down onto the beach, below the Holyhead Breakwater, to see the excellently displayed tight folds in the New Harbour Formation schists.

At the Breakwater Country Park, to your west is the towering mountain of the Holyhead Quartzite that has been extensively quarried in the area below. At this distance you can see the vertical lines that represent the rough *cleavage* that dominates much of the quartzite, whereas bedding, that is subhorizontal to shallow dipping, is detectable from coarse partings, as also seen in Figure 1. The Holyhead Quartzite lies on the SW side of a major fault that runs through Porth Namarch, the bay ahead of you, and this fault feature continues NW – SE across Holy Island. The quartzite is exposed in overgrown quarries behind the visitor centre and can also be seen in some of the large blocks in the car park. The area around one abandoned quarry later became a brickworks making high silica bricks for furnaces, and here you can see a display and the remains of kilns and the towering chimneys (Figure 1).

There is a well-used signposted coastal footpath from the visitor centre that goes over the mountain of Holyhead Quartzite to South Stack, which is the best way to see the rock in situ. However, keeping this excursion close to the Country Park, we suggest you take the path from the westernmost car park past the lake towards the coast edge to join the coastal path. Then taking the coastal path a little way to the left, at [225835] you get a good view down into Porth Namarch, eroded along the line of the *fault* (Figure 2). The dark-coloured stack in the bay is a remnant of a *dolerite dyke* that extends SE along the length of Holy island. You

2. View from the cliff-top looking north into Porth Namarch where a fault separates the Holyhead Quartzite on the left from the Rhoscolyn Formation sandstones on the right. The small dark-coloured stack on the right is the eroded remnants of a dolerite dyke.

will get an even better view of the fault gully and of the whole coast to the east towards Holyhead, if you take the coastal path for about 400m to the west, to reach a viewpoint at the cliff edge at [224836] framed by the quartzite (Figure 3), before the path turn uphill via steps. This gives another perspective on the Porth Namarch fault gully and dyke remnant, and also a distant view of the enclosed bay described next and shown in Figure 4.

3. View east from the coastal path viewpoint at [224836] looking through a natural wall of Holyhead Quartzite across to Porth Namarch (see Figure 2, taken from another direction) and the coastline towards Holyhead. The small bay that is the site of Figures 4-6 is arrowed.

Returning to take the path that goes down to the edge of the coast from the Visitor Centre above, you have crossed the line of the fault through Porth Namarch on to the Rhoscolyn Formation on its NE side. Continue along the coastal path eastwards for about 200m until near a small wooden bridge, where below you will see a small enclosed bay located in Figure 3 [227835]. Descending with care into this attractive bay, you will find an interesting variety of sediments at this locality (Figure 4). The variously coloured rocks in this bay were deposited in a channel within the purer more typical sandstones of the Rhoscolyn Formation, and give a unique view of sedimentary structures within the

4. *Rhoscolyn Formation sediments in the small bay at [227835], showing a brown mudstone-siltstone knoll by the person, extreme right, where sedimentary structures and Figure 5 are seen. Figure 6 is just off the front-left. Looking east.*

formation, such as *ripple-drift laminations* and lobate bases that are *load structures* (Figure 5), as well as locally developed *conglomerates*. The beds are right-way up and gently folded with a weak *axial-plane cleavage* developed that you can see at the west end of the bay (Figure 6).

Returning to the coastal path, there is a pleasant walk to the east across the Rhoscolyn Formation. Descending where you can onto the coastal ledges, you will see that the bedding in the formation is nearly horizontal, with locally developed vertical cleavage and open *minor folds*. Alternatively, return to the car park from here.

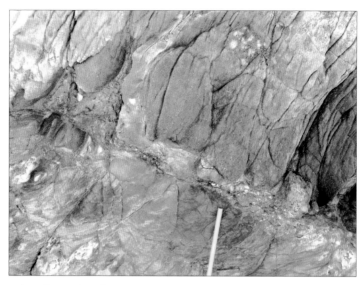

5. *Lobate base of a siltstone bed, in the knoll where ripple-drift structures are also seen; looking west.*

6. *Bedding and cleavage relationships in sandstones and mudstones in the Rhoscolyn Formation, looking NE. Cleavage is steeply SE-dipping, and bedding shallowly SE-dipping.*

N. Trwyn y Parc, Cemaes

This excursion provides a most pleasant walk along the cliff tops and then a descent into an old limestone quarry. It is concerned with the presence of a number of pipes – or pot holes – in this limestone, the Gwna Limestone of the Mona Complex. It provides not only an opportunity to examine the limestone but also to see these unusual features of the Anglesey landscape. The pipes are a product of *karstic* weathering of the limestone by ground-water solution in the early Cenozoic about 60 million years ago, the time when a variety of mammals began to roam the landscape. The pipes have been subsequently filled with material dating from the Early Neogene Period some 5.3 million years ago. The pipes, of which 15 have been recognised, are estimated to

*1. View of the quarry on the foreshore looking south. Pipes **a** (water-filled) and **b** (pebble filled), on the right side, in front of standing figure, and **d** (drift-filled, back left) are discussed in the text. Two smaller pipes are seen in the centre foreground.*

have a minimum depth of 12m, judged from heights of the highest and lowest pipes. The pipes are overlain by undisturbed deposits from the last major glaciation of the Quaternary, some 80,000-10,000 years ago.

Take the A55 from Britannia Bridge and in about 25km take exit 3 for the A5, signposted Valley, to the crossroads in that village. Turn right at the traffic lights on the A5025 at Valley, signposted to Amlwch. Continue over the roundabout at Cemaes, and in just over 1 km turn left on a narrow road, signposted to the Gadlys Hotel and P(arking), a kilometre before the town. After 1km take the sharp left turning signposted again with a P and after another kilometre park in the large free carpark at [375938] by the pleasant bay. Follow the signposted National Trust coastal footpath that goes up the cliff and along the top northwards some 400m, to a lime kiln, at the east end of an old lime quarry on the shore [373941].

The description below is based on the once quarried wave-cut platform (Figures 1 and 2) and the adjacent cliff sections. On the wave-cut platform the two largest and most obvious horizontal sections of pipes make hollow circular features (**a** and **b** on Figure 2), seen on the right-hand side of Figure 1; pipe **b** is 6m across and has a filling of yellow clay and boulders. Adjacent to pipe **a**, several smaller pipe necks (e.g. at **c**) are seen, and to the northeast of pipe **b** are other small hollows, presumed to be pipe necks. The exposed sides of these pipes are almost vertical, although in some instances slightly inward-dipping. The original fill of many of these pipes is not exposed, being filled with water, although some are partly filled by limestone boulders and stones in a matrix of yellow-grey clay. Most puzzling is a pipe opening a few metres inland from the two large pipe necks (**c** on Figure 2); this is about a metre across and occupied by a boulder composed of sub-rounded quartzite fragments 1-20cm across in a sandy dark matrix. The boulder could have been derived from the melange on the Llanbadrig peninsula (see Llanbadrig excursion)

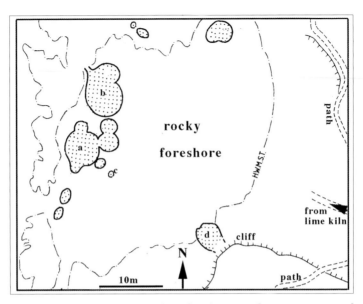

2. *Map of the Trwyn y Parc site. The pipes are shown ornamented;*
a, **b**, **c** *and* **d** *are discussed in the text.*

to the north during the Quaternary and been transported into the pipe opening.

The best vertical section across a pipe, some 5m in visible depth, is on the cliff face 20m SE of the kiln (**d** on Figure 2; Figure 3). The left side of the pipe is well-seen with detached blocks of limestone resulting from the karstic erosion at the top and black and brown clay below. The black material is clay and stained fine-grained quartz, whilst the brown material is gibbsite (a clay–like mineral) and goethite (an iron oxide derived from clays), both products of tropical weathering. The main fill to the right is a fine *breccia* that includes igneous fragments, as well as white calcite and quartz fragments 1-2cm across, in a clay matrix. The right margin of the pipe is not exposed, but the pipe must have been at least four metres across and shows a narrowing downwards. The pipe is truncated above by a covering of Irish Sea *till* of the last major glaciation of the Quaternary. Other vertical sections of

3. The north margin of pipe **d** showing some of its karstic fill at top and the black clay fill below. To the right is the pebbly clay of the centre of the pipe. Notebook is 16cm long. The lime kiln is visible in the background.

pipes, with blackened clay fill and truncated by glacial till, are to be seen in the cliffs both to the north and south of the quarries.

The pipes are cut into the Gwna Limestone, excellently exposed throughout these quarry and cliff sections. This is a fine-grained blue-grey calcite limestone, in some beds graphitic and often well-laminated (Figure 4); some of this lamination has been recognised as being of *stromatolitic* origin by geologists in 1973, who also identified spheroidal microfossils of the same type as those illustrated in Figure 2 of the Llanbadrig Excursion. In the southwest, the limestone *dips* moderately NE, steepening to almost vertical in the northeast. This area of limestone is part of an extraordinary chaotic *melange* of rocks, *quartzite*, limestone, mudstone, sandstone and volcanics within the Gwna Group, that is seen particularly well in the Llanbadrig Peninsula less than 1km to the north. It has been proposed to be part of the process of the *subduction* of ocean floor in the late Precambrian and Lower Palaeozoic.

You can return the way you came, or combine this excursion with Llanbadrig, via a pleasant walk of about 1km along the coastal path.

*4. Laminated Gwna Limestone, showing possible stromatolitic features, to the right of pipe **d**. The pen is 10cm long.*

O. Llanbadrig

This excursion examines one of the most sensational geological localities on Anglesey, the rocks on the steep northern coast of this headland offering the finest view of the spectacular Gwna Melange, the youngest rocks in the Mona Complex. This *melange* consists of a jumble of blocks, ranging in size from several tens of metres in greatest length down to those a few centimetres across, of *quartzite*, limestone, mudstones and siltstones. It is thought to be the product of submarine slumping and *brecciation* of partially solidified deposits on the sea floor, due to instability of the sedimentary slope, perhaps triggered by an earthquake in the late Precambrian. Similar rocks can be seen on the Llanddwyn Island excursion. You will also see the fossilised remains of Precambrian algae.

Take the A55 from Britannia Bridge and in about 25km take exit 3 for the A5, signposted Valley, to the crossroads in that village. Turn right at the traffic lights on the A5025 at Valley, signposted to Amlwch. Continue for some 22km to the roundabout at Cemaes; go straight over and in just over 1 km turn left on a narrow road, signposted to the Gadlys Hotel and with a P(arking). Ignore the turning left to a large carpark at Cemaes Bay, but after 1km bear left to Llanbadrig church, where there is a small carpark [375946] that gives easy access to the peninsula. At weekends and holiday times this small carpark quickly becomes full; the alternative is to use the large car park at [375937] referred to above and take the pleasant 1km coastal footpath, that also gives access to the nearby locality described at Trwyn y Parc.

The church adjacent to the small carpark is of interest. Dedicated to St Patrick (Padrig in Welsh), the original church on the site is believed to have been founded by Patrick, who had been sent to convert Ireland to Christianity in the 14th century. He is said to have been shipwrecked off the coast, but made his way to a cave beneath the site of the present church. The church has features of the 14th and 16th century, but was largely restored in the 19th century. The peninsula is owned by the National Trust and access to the pleasant grassy cliff-top is completely unrestricted. All of the exposures can be accessed without descending any of the steep cliffs although some scrambling on the cliff-top is required.

1. *Geological map of the Llanbadrig peninsular showing, bottom right, the access road and car park. Areas 1-4, discussed in the text, are shown circled. The two interrupted lines are presumed faults separating areas 1-2, 3, and 4.*

This description starts at the eastern end of the peninsula and progresses along the northern coast. It can be divided into three areas of outcrop, which are characterised, from east to west, by limestone, *phyllite* (originally mudstone and siltstone) and quartzite (originally sandstone) labelled 1-2, 3 and 4 on Figure 1.

Grey limestone forms the principal rock type that makes up the eastern block of the melange, from [375946] to [373446] between

116

the church and the main area of phyllite. This mass is over 200m across, west to east, 60m north to south and, at a minimum, 25 metres high. The limestone is well-seen in a small quarry that you enter if you take the path from the carpark to the north, and around the adjacent disused lime kiln [375046]. It is a calcitic limestone, sometimes exhibiting delicate bedding, marked by thin layers of dark phyllite, but in which no fossils have been discovered. However, on the pavement in front of the kiln the limestone has a most interesting gritty appearance as seen in Figure 2; with a hand-lens these mm-sized spots are seen to be spherical to elliptical bodies that generally might be identified as *oolites*. In fact, under the microscope, and even with a hand-lens, some can be seen to have subdivisions; they are more correctly describe as *oncoliths*, rolled algal fragments. Other parts of the limestone here can be seen to be laminated, a feature of *stromatolitic* structure. Stromatolites are laminated accretionary structures of blue-green algae, often wavy in appearance; these

2. *Limestone at area 1, showing fragmental stromatolitic and oncolitic structures. Top of coin at bottom of picture is 2cm across.*

are also observed at the western end of the limestone, as discussed below. They are the oldest known fossils, ranging in age from 3.5 million years to the present day; here they are probably latest Precambrian to early Cambrian (about 600-500 million years) in age.

Bedding in the limestone is locally seen as thin beds of dark mudstone, steeply ENE-dipping, sometimes folded, but cleavage is not usually developed. The limestone often exhibits *stylolites* and cross-cutting calcite veins. The wall of the kiln is interesting as it contains blocks of the local limestone containing tight folds that are not readily seen in outcrop. A dolerite dyke is seen to the west of the kiln, about 10m thick. Several such dykes of Tertiary age, trending NW-SE, cut the sequence described below. The one at the kiln is coarse-grained but very heavily altered and branching; others to the west are a finer-grained dolerite.

The accessible exposure of limestone (area 1 - 2 on Figure 1) along the top of the cliff between the kiln and the main outcrop of phyllite (area 3 on Figure 1), seen 150m to the west and described below, is a mixture of limestone, *dolomite* and phyllite. Within the limestone unit immediately to the west of the kiln are bodies of dolomite distinguished from the limestone by its resistance to dilute acid. Contacts of the limestone with the dolomite bodies are sometimes gradational but elsewhere appear to be fractures; these bodies probably resulted from magnesium-rich solutions permeating the limestone. There is also one body tens of metres across of yellow/orange-coloured sideritic limestone, rich in the iron carbonate *siderite* (Figure 3); this, similarly, is probably a result of iron-rich solutions permeating the limestone. Near the junction with the main phyllite unit [373446] discussed below, the limestone contains delicate bedding on a cm and mm-scale, which could indicate stromatolitic structure. There are also small bodies of grey shale, a metre or two across, and cleaved phyllite up to 20m long. One of the phyllite bodies is well-seen just to the north and northwest of the lime kiln.

3. One of the bodies, here about 2m thick, of orange-coloured siderite within the grey limestone of area 2; looking NE.

The phyllite mass immediately west of the junction with the limestone (area 3 on Figure 1), is where the main features of the melange are seen. There are areas crowded with small clasts of quartzite and blocks of cleaved muddy siltstone that locally contain distinct, thin (cm-mm scale) beds; the latter sometimes exhibit small-scale tight folds, to which the cleavage is axial-planar. The most spectacular features of the melange in the phyllite are metre-length boulders of white quartzite elongate in the ESE-striking, steep-dipping, cleavage, as well as isolated quartzite blocks up to 15m in length (Figure 4). A notable feature of the phyllite in the bay just west of the junction, is the presence of several small pits from which *jasper* has been extracted. The jasper is not very visible if the pits are flooded by rain-water, but consists of lens-shaped bedded bodies several centimetres thick; the rock was highly prized for making into ornaments. Jasper is similarly associated with the melange at Llanddwyn Island.

To the west of the main phyllite body is an area (4 on Figure 1) dominated by one major body of white quartzite and a spectacular train of white quartzite boulders, a metre or two in length. One large block of quartzite, some 20m across, makes an impressive isolated stack at [373946], just off the northern coast of the phyllite unit, accessible, with care, at low tide.

If you choose to return via the southern edge of the peninsula, on the cliff top is a series of small quartzite blocks, probably in *situ*, a metre or so across. This train possibly continues in the sporadic outcrops and loose blocks of quartzite along the southern coast, extending to a spectacular stack, called White Lady, at [376945] on the far southeast part of the coast (Figure 5).

4. The melange in area 3, looking NE. In the centre is part of a train of large quartzite blocks, with smaller blocks in the phyllite in the foreground; the phyllite in the background is crowded with even smaller blocks.

The precise context of the melange in the sedimentary and tectonic history of Anglesey is still a subject of dispute. The melange has been proposed to be part of the process of the subduction of ocean floor in the late Precambrian and Lower Palaeozoic.

5. The "White Lady" on the southern shore of the Llanbadrig peninsula.

P. Porth Wen

Porth Wen is on the north coast of Anglesey, approximately halfway between Cemaes and Amlwch. This place was once a hive of industry, where high silica refractory bricks were made using the local white *quartzite*, and exported by sea from the works' own harbour. The brickworks operated from 1850 to 1914, over which time many buildings and towers, including beehive-shaped firing kilns that remain today (Figure 1) were built, as well as a winding station to take the local rock down to the production area. The harbour was hazardous, however, and a contributing factor in the decline of Porth Wen's brickworks. The Old Brickworks remain as a reminder of Anglesey's industrial heritage, a stunning landmark on this part of Anglesey's coast that is encountered by those who are walking on the Coastal Path from Llanbadrig to Amlwch, or those making a special visit as described here.

Although we shall see the white quartzite that gave Porth Wen its name, and was the reason the brickworks developed here, this locality is also one of the best places on Anglesey to see the *unconformity* between the Precambrian Gwna Group schists and quartzites and Ordovician Arenig conglomerate of the Porth Cynfor Formation. The *conglomerate* here is a similar age, but a rather different appearance, from the Ordovician conglomerate that is seen on the Rhosneigr excursion.

Directions are based on the assumption that you will make this a single excursion. However, those who are undertaking a long walk on the Anglesey Coastal Path can approach this locality from Llanbadrig 3 km to the west (see Llanbadrig excursion), or from Amlwch 3 km to the east. This would confine you to the coast, omitting the first locality shown in Figure 2.

From the Britannia Bridge, take the exit after 1km for the A5025

1. *Part of the Old Brickworks at Porth Wen, looking west,
with white quartzite in the cliffs behind. This is a 'beehive' kiln.*

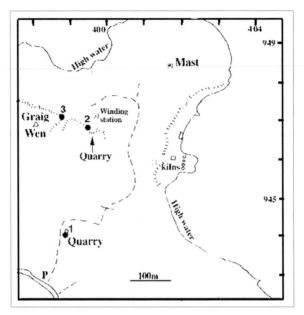

2. Sketch map of Porth Wen site showing localities 1-3 and landmarks. The access road and parking (P) is bottom left; dashed lines are paths referred to in text.

to Amlwch. Four km west of Amlwch, on your right there is a very poorly signposted minor road that leaves the A5025 at [401936]; after 1km, at a bend, there is limited parking for cars on the roadside at [398943]. Alternatively, if coming from areas to the west along the A5025, after the roundabout turning to Cemaes continue for about 3km to the minor road mentioned above. From the parking area there are two footpaths; take the one to the left, next to a large gate, and proceed to the north some 200m until you reach a small quarry on your right (Figure 2).

Locality 1
The right hand lower side of the small quarry at [399944] (Figure 2) provides a rare opportunity to see schists of the Skerries Formation, a member of the Gwna Group. These are chlorite-biotite schists with a steeply N-dipping *schistosity*; bedding is not clear. They are overlain and *hornfelsed* here by a green-coloured

124

sill of dolerite composition that has been quarried; the edge of the sill shares the *cleavage* that affects the underlying schists confirming that it predates the *metamorphism*.

Proceed through a swing gate, next to a double gate, to the cliff-top with a view of the disused beehive-shaped brick kilns on the beach below (Figure 1) and of the Gwna Group white quartzite on the hill to your left (Figure 3), the important component for the brickmaking endeavour here.

Keep on the main path which curves uphill towards the winding station at [400947] for localities on the Graig Wen ridge. Leave the path to go to the quarry behind the winding station (Figure 2), where the white quartzite was extracted and sent down to the brickworks below in former times.

3. *The white Gwna Group quartzite in the quarry at locality 2, looking west, with the unconformity and overlying Porth Cynfor conglomerate seen on the far right.*

4. The Ordovician conglomerate at locality 2 looking west, showing the elongation of the mainly quartzite clasts in the N-dipping cleavage.

Locality 2

The first outcrops here, at the edge of an abandoned quarry at [400947], show some of the best exposures of the unconformity between the Gwna Group quartzites and the overlying Porth Cynfor Arenig conglomeratic grits. Figure 3 shows the brilliant white quartzite has a crude sedimentary layering dipping gently to the north and the uncomformable junction with the conglomerates, marked by the blue pen in Figure 3, dipping steeply N. Bedding in the conglomerates is difficult to see but a crude layering dips quite steeply N, and is crossed by a rough *cleavage* that is much steeper-dipping N. This relationship of cleavage to bedding is seen clearly in nearby exposures of the conglomerate (Figure 4). Here the bedding is parallel to the two bounding surfaces of the exposure, while the fine-grained matrix to the conglomerate defines the steeper N-dipping cleavage; the elongation of the *clasts* is clearly parallel to this cleavage.

The well-defined escarpment above the path defines the junction between the conglomerate and poorly-exposed grits and mudstones to the north. The rock has a striking purplish appearance (Figure 4), probably due to its dark red *jasper* content, although most of the visible clasts are quartzite in a gritty matrix. About 100m along the edge of the scarp westwards, there is a gap in exposure where a path crosses from the south. On the west side of the gap there is another clear exposure of conglomerate, which is the next locality (Figure 2).

5. *Close-up of the conglomerate at locality 3, showing the elongation of the clasts in the cleavage with their elongated "tails". The large clasts are of stained quartzite and there are small red jasper clasts in the matrix.*

Locality 3

Here, the Arenig Porth Cynfor conglomerate in seen again in discordant contact with the Gwna Group quartzite. The unconformity surface, as well as both bedding and cleavage in the schistose conglomerate, are here about vertical and E-W striking, while bedding in the quartzite, although obscure in the heavily quartz-veined quartzite, dips moderately N.

The conglomerate exposure has a similar appearance to the previous locality, with a pronounced steeply N-dipping cleavage in the matrix, that bowes around the hard clasts that are dominantly quartzite, with lesser grit, jasper and phyllite. The clasts are elongate (elliptical or rhomboid) viewed perpendicular to the cleavage (Figures 4 & 5), with diameter ratios of more than 2 to 1, consistent with the Caledonian deformation that produced the cleavage here, and contemporary with folding overlying non-conglomeratic rocks. Some of the clasts exhibit pronounced tails at their ends in the long direction of the clasts and into the cleavage (Figure 5), which in thin-section are seen to be of recrystallised quartz.

By detailed observation all along the ridge we have seen both 1m-thick beds of conglomerate in the quartzite as well as similarly-sized units of quartzite in the conglomerate. This is quite a complicated unconformity with a significant dip northwards, probable an irregular topography, as well as this apparent interleaving of the conglomerate and quartzite, some of which may be due to faulting. This is an important unconformity, marking a break between the Gwna quartzite that is presumed to be Precambrian, and the Ordovician Porth Cynfor Formation of Arenig age (470Ma).

The exposures at Porth Wen are important in the controversy concerning the nature of the break between the Mona Complex and the overlying Lower Palaeozoic rocks on Anglesey. Although the deformation history of the Gwna Group rocks is not easy to study here, nearby exposures in schistose grits to the south of Graig Wen that locally contain quartzite clasts show the same deformational history as described above. They exhibit upright E-W folding associated with a single axial-planar cleavage, and the deformed clasts show similar elongated shapes to those noted above in the Porth Cynfor conglomerate. So although the break between the Mona Complex and the overlying Lower Palaeozoic rocks has been traditionally considered as a major tectonic unconformity, the two rock units here suffered a common Caledonian deformation. The Gwna Group rocks were deformed by tilting, and perhaps gentle folding, before the deposition of the Ordovician, but from what we see at Porth Wen, the major orogenic event – the Caledonian deformation, resulting in upright E-W folding and axial-planar cleavage – affected both rock units. One caveat is that the identity and age of the supposed Gwna Group rocks at this site, in relation to those elsewhere on Anglesey, as well as the relations of the melanges seen on the Llanbadrig and Llanddwyn excursions, is far from certain.

Q. Amlwch

This excursion is written mostly to persuade you to go to the GeoMôn Visitor Centre, formerly the Watch House down in the old harbour [450935] (Figure 1). This is open daily from 11 to 4 and contains excellent displays as well as books and leaflets concerning local geology. GeoMôn also has an excellent web site (http://www.geomon.co.uk/) that will tell you more about the geology of Anglesey.

1. The old watch house at the mouth of the harbour, now the GeoMôn visitor centre. The rocks beyond are exposures of the Amlwch Formation on the west side of the harbour.

The small town owes its development to ship building, but particularly to the need in the 18th and 19th centuries to find an outlet for the developing copper mines at Parys Mountain (see excursion). Originally a small fishing harbour, Port Amlwch was developed by Act of Parliament in 1793 into a major port for the export of copper and eventually a centre for ship-building and

2. *The schists of the Amlwch Formation just east of the car park at [453936] looking east. The cleavage dips steeper to the north than the bedding, which can be seen above and parallel to the pencil.*

repair. The separated copper was transported by horse and cart from the mine, down a track for some 3km, and refined in smelters at Amlwch. It was then transported as ingots to Liverpool and Swansea, from where coal was imported.

Geologically, the Port and surrounding coast has outcrops of the Amlwch Formation, a *schistose* brown-coloured rock, comprising *muscovite* and fine *quartz* alternating with cm-mm thick beds of white-coloured *quartzite*. The dip of the *schistosity* is steep to the north. In clean exposure around the harbour, especially on paths on its west side (Figure 1), you may be able to see tight folds, and *faults* with small displacements are also well seen in places. However, the best exposure of the Formation is seen on the cliffs to the east of the town [453936] (Figure 2). Immediately beyond the parking area at the end of the cliff top road to the east of the town, you can see in the rocks on the cliff that the schistosity *dips* slightly steeper to the north than the bedding. You may also be able to discern tight to *isoclinal folds* to which the schistosity is *axial-planar*. This schist is supposed to be equivalent to the schists of the New Harbour Formation that you may have seen on Holy Island (Treaddur Bay, Porth y Pwll and Porth y Post excursions).

An even better view of the Amlwch Formation can be had by taking a pleasant walk eastwards, through the gate at the end of the car park, another kilometre or so on to the hill around [456935]. Here there are well-displayed, tight, folds of the bedding and schistosity, again overfolding to the south and consistent with the bedding and schistosity relations you have seen near the car park.

R. Parys Mountain

This is one of the most dramatic landscapes anywhere in the British Isles – it has been compared, justifiably, with a moonscape, as seen in Figure 1. There is evidence of Bronze-age and Roman mining but the main period of working was from 1768 to 1883, in which time the mine was the principal source of copper in Europe. By 1920 all mining had ceased although precipitation from the copper waste continued to the 1950s. It should be emphasised that there is very little sign of the copper minerals that made this mine so important. What copper minerals there were in veins in the pit, the Great Opencast, have been efficiently removed over the 2000 years of mining history; the current economic interest in the area is purely in proven underground deposits. The nearby coastal port of Amlwch, 3km to the north, was developed by Act of Parliament in 1793 into a

1. View of the Great Opencast from the viewpoint looking NE.
Points of interest are discussed in the text.

major port for the export of the separated copper, which was transported by horse and cart from the mine, down a track, and refined in smelters at Amlwch. The Amlwch excursion would make a very suitable accompaniment to this excursion.

From the Britannia Bridge, on the A55, in 1km take the A5025 northwards. In about 20km, just before reaching Amlwch, you will see on your left the dramatic feature of the Parys Mountain copper mines. Just after the town sign for Amlwch, at [445918], take a minor road to your left, with a brown signpost for "Leisure Centre". In 0.5km turn left on the B5111 and in 1.5km you will see another brown signpost for "Copper-mine Trail" and a car park sign (P) for Parys Mountain on your left. If you are coming to the mine from Amlwch, from the roundabout on the A5025 south of the town, take the B5111 southwards for 2.5 km where you will see on your left a car park sign (P) for Parys Mountain. In the car park you will find a dispenser providing a very informative leaflet (25p) concerning the history of the Parys Mountain Copper Mines with a plan of arrowed and numbered trail posts around this dramatic colourful area.

In brief, the geological history of the area (Figure 2) appears to be as follows, though some details are disputed. The rocks in the area of the pit are underlain by the Mona Complex and the succeeding lower parts of the Ordovician; the latter are shales and mudstones of Arenig to Llanvirn age (about 470 million years), the Parys Shales, only seen in poor exposures in areas NW and SE of the mining area. In both areas those rocks dip steeply NNW, forming the limbs of a *syncline* with an overturned northwesterly *limb* (Figures 2 & 3). The succeeding mudstones and shales that host volcanic lava and ash (*tuff*), forming the core of the syncline, are probably of uppermost Ordovician age (Caradocian, about 450 million years) though fossil evidence is scant. Low down in the succession the mined ores occurred as layers, veins and massive lenses; higher up where we are looking, the ores occur in a series of lenses and veins in shales and *cherts*,

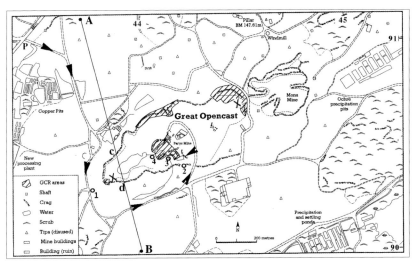

2. *Map of the Great Opencast; A – B marks part of the line of the cross-section in Figure 3. P = parking and arrow-heads show the route suggested in the text. Points 1 - 4 are referred to in the text.*

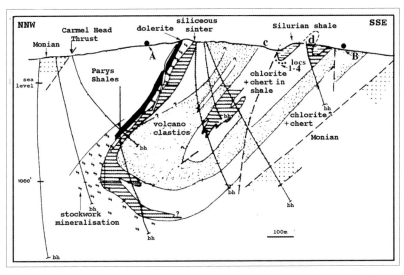

3. *Cross-section of the Great Opencast on which points A & B and c-d on Figure 2 are shown.*

together with minor *rhyolite* lava. These ores are dominantly *pyrite* with lesser *chalcopyrite, sphalerite* and *galena* and rare *tetrahedrite* and lead-bismuth minerals. The Ordovician rocks in the core of the syncline are succeeded by Silurian shales and siltstones of Llandovery age (about 440 million years); in these rocks, owing to tight folding, the cleavage is nearly parallel to bedding, so that *graptolites* (*monograptids*) are well-preserved and can be found here. The sediments and mineralised layers were folded into a tight syncline as shown in Figure 3, in the *Caledonian Orogeny* (390 million years ago) when some ore minerals were remobilised to form sulphide-*quartz*-chlorite veins and silica-rich fluids permeated, giving the rocks generally a cherty appearance. This type of mineralization is similar to the Miocene type-deposit in western Japan, where magma has been intruded into sediments under or onto the sea floor. The heat from this intrusion would cause hot water to circulate through the rocks concentrating minerals such as iron, copper, lead and zinc which, combining with sulphur, crystallised in veins or as more widely disseminated ores through the sediments.

Follow the arrowed path from the car park, passing the old water-filled copper precipitation pits. By the track-side there is plentiful loose material containing fine-grained golden pyrite and if you are lucky brownish sphalerite; but there is very little sign of copper mineralization. If you are very lucky you might find the brassy copper pyrite (chalcopyrite) or the usually common secondary carbonates, green malachite or blue azurite. Here and elsewhere in the mine you also rarely find silvery galena, the lead sulphide. Just before the viewing platform at trail post 1, there is an excellent track-side exposure of flow-banding in rhyolite, dipping steeply to the southeast and locally folded. These rhyolite lavas, that form the lowest part of the volcanic succession, are only seen at this end of the pit.

From the view-point [439902] (see Figure 2, point 1) you get a dramatic view of the Great Opencast, looking NE, and there is an informative explanation board concerning its history. The colours of the outcrop and waste material vary from purple to red to orange to yellow and grey, depending on the oxidation state of the weathered iron-rich sulphides. Assuming that the original ground surface was level with the top of the pit, an astonishing amount of material has been excavated. The two black holes in the lower and upper right of the pit are the entrances to old trial workings. In the centre of the pit you can see the ruins of some of the 19th century mine buildings in the area of the localities we will visit subsequently.

You might be able to distinguish, just below the sky-line in the centre, at the very far eastern end, the syncline in the Silurian shales that forms the basis of the structure. The western end of the syncline is in the quarry-side just beneath your feet, as we shall see later. To the right you can see that cleavage, dipping to the northwest, dominates the Silurian rocks.

Follow the arrowed trail around the south side of the pit (see arrowed route on Figure 2). As you walk around the top of the pit you will notice the orange to red colour of the ponds and streams resulting from mine drainage, owing to their high acidity resulting from the high concentration of sulphuric acid. After about 600 metres you will come to a track turning down into the pit on your left, about 20m before a green arrow trail marker No. 2; to your right you will see the ruins of the 19th century mine offices. Descend the track for 100m until you come to a small rough path leading down to your left (Figure 1, point 2). Proceed down the path for about 20m until you get a view to your left of an old *adit* entrance, one of the several blocked entrances to the extensive underground workings, from which most of the copper was recovered; this adit was recently re-excavated. In the loose specimens of the silvery Silurian slates you may find some monograptid fossils. In front of the adit is one of several settling ponds you will see on the pit floor, and beyond are the remains of mine buildings.

4. View of the SW end of the Great Opencast pit. The central boss is to the right of the path and the adit and adjacent exposures described in the text, to the left.

Returning down to the main path (Figure 1, point 3) you get a good view of the SW end of the pit (Figure 3). The main boss in the centre, to the right of the path (Figure 4), is composed of heavily pyritised black cherty sediment cross-cut by quartz veins (Figure 5). To the south and left of the path, there is another trial adit entrance, this one blind. These sediments are followed north in the outcrop by chert beds, which are heavily pyritised. In many of the exposures at this locality, small grains of galena and sphalerite as well as of chalcopyrite may be found. Walk beyond the central boss to its west (Figure 1, point 4), where you will get a good close-up view of the western end of the pit. At its far southern side you will see the western end of the main synclinal fold in the Silurian shales, showing well-developed axial-planar cleavage.

5. The side of the central boss. Chert in a shaley matrix, crossed by pyritic quartz veins; the quartz vein at the base and right of the exposure is parallel to bedding.

Return to the main path at the top of the pit if you intend to return to your vehicle; if you are not in a hurry, the signposts will take you on a long but pleasant walk around the whole pit outcrop.

S. Lligwy

Lligwy Bay is one of the largest sandy bays on the eastern shore of Anglesey. The rocks on its southern shore are Carboniferous Limestone, that are exposed all the way to Red Wharf Bay, and can be seen at Moelfre, Traeth Bychan, and Benllech Bay. The north side of the bay has a different appearance. The rocks are interbedded red sandstones, siltstones and mudstones of supposed lower Devonian age, although no fossils or *radiometric dates* are known. The interest here is in the origin of these unusual sedimentary rocks, and particularly in their structure. You will see evidence of dramatic folding, and the formation of related cleavage in these lower Devonian rocks, which we attribute to the *Acadian Orogeny* in the mid-Devonian, about 400 million years ago.

This excursion is based on the accessible cliffs that stretch for about 0.5km at the back of a very pleasant sandy beach, but you do need a low to medium tide, especially at the northern end. The map (Figure 1) shows the high-water line at the foot of the cliff where the numbered localities that are described below are seen. The cross-section is approximately perpendicular to the strike of the beds.

If you are coming on the A55 from the Britannia Bridge, take the second exit signposted for the A5025 towards Amlwch. After about 25 km, at a small roundabout just outside Moelfre, turn left and continue on the Amlwch road but after 3km take the minor road on your right at Brynrefail [480869] signposted, obscurely, to Lligwy. This narrow road will bring you after 2km to Lligwy beach car park [494877]; out-of-season (at least November to March), and in poor weather, this car park apparently is free, otherwise there is a £2 charge (at the time of writing). It is a short distance to another car park to the south, where there are seasonal toilets and a café.

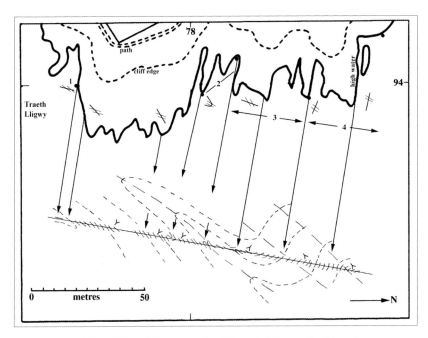

1. *Map of the cliff and shore north of Traeth Lligwy, looking due west. The heavy line is the high tide line at the foot of the cliff, around which dots mark the limits of localities 1-4. The symbols around the edge of the cliff indicate relations of bedding (heavy line) to cleavage (fine line pairs) as viewed on the vertical cliff face, looking towards the WNW. This information is projected onto the cross-section beneath the map, where the short lines indicate the observed dip of bedding and the Y symbols point towards younger rocks, from the evidence of sedimentary structures. Long broken lines indicate the axial planes of the major folds.*

Go down to the beach from the car park and walk north over sand and muddy drift deposits to the first rock exposures, the alternating red siltstones and sandstones of the Traeth Lligwy Beds.

Locality 1: synclinal hinge into overturned limb of a major recumbent anticline

In the very first 10m of exposure, below the dunes, the beds are flat-lying and appear, from ripple-drift *cross-bedding* and *sun-*

141

2. Sun-cracked right-way-up bedding surfaces at locality 1; above the notebook the beds turn up to a vertical attitude around a syncline, with a fault to their immediate right. Looking WNW.

crack structures, to be the right-way-up. Immediately before the main cliff starts, these beds turn up vertically around a small *synclinal* fold (Figure 2) with a steep, N-dipping fault to its right. This outcrop is interpreted here as the beginning of the overturned limb of the main *recumbent anticline*, as shown on the cross-section. In the next 80m of cliff exposure, the alternating thin-bedded red sandstones and siltstones *dip* at moderate angles to the north. They have a 'burrowed' appearance with branching tubes of more silty material in the sandstones, but it is difficult to see whether these are truncated, so that they might be used to determine the 'way-up' of the beds. Another contrasting feature with sandstones we will see further north is that the beds are thinner and rather discontinuous; cross-bedding is difficult to find, but a few examples do show that the beds are inverted. The dip is now at various angles to the north and although there are no minor *folds*, intriguingly, as you progress northwards it is increasingly apparent that there is a *cleavage*; this is seen in the thin muddy siltstones between the dominant sandstones and consistently dips at shallower angle than the bedding (Figure 3). This is, of course, purely structural evidence, but it supports the evidence from the cross-bedding observations that we are on an inverted sequence of beds.

3. Looking WNW at steep N-dipping beds with cleavage dipping at a consistently shallower angle N, at locality 1.

4. The anticlinal complex broken by N-dipping thrusts at locality 2, looking WNW.

Locality 2: Folds and cleavage in the overturned limb of the major recumbent anticline

On the beach, beyond a small gap in exposure, there is a clearly displayed syncline with a steep N-dipping northern limb and axial-planar cleavage as we have seen at the previous locality. The syncline is also seen in the cliff behind. "Way-up" is not easy to find, but there is one 20cm thick bed showing good inverted ripple-drift cross-lamination some 8m north of the syncline, under the cliff by a large grey boulder. The beds steepen towards the little bay further north, with a NW-dipping cleavage consistently flatter than the bedding, where there is a complex anticlinal structure associated with *thrusts* (Figure 4). These observations, the cleavage relationships and the inverted cross-lamination, imply that we have been consistently walking along the inverted limb of what must be a major anticline.

Locality 3: the right-way-up limb

The reality of this anticline can now be demonstrated, as the beds on the platform below the cliff in the next section of exposures now dip gently north, and all the evidence shows that these beds are the right-way-up. Some of the beds exhibit right-way-up sun-cracks on the top surfaces (Figure 5) and there are also right-way-up *ripple drift laminations*. Cleavage now dips steeply north, so we are definitely now in the complementary, right-way-up, limb of the major anticline, the upside-down limb of which we have seen in the previous localities. In the cliff there is an interesting small anticline with a thrust at its base (Figure 6) and some small normal faults (see cross-section). The beds then show a gentle syncline/anticline structure but are generally undulating, with an overall flat dip.

5. Sun-cracks on a gently N-dipping bedding surface at locality 3.

6. *Minor anticline in sun-cracked sandstone, overturned south above a thrust (visible in right foreground) at locality 3. Looking west.*

Locality 4: folds in the continuation of the right-way-up limb

Continuing along the beach edge, the rocks are seen to gradually turn into a progressively steeper southerly dip, becoming vertical and even slightly overturned northwards, and show a nice example of *cleavage refraction* with a shallow northerly dip (Figure 7); we are on the south limb of another major anticline. Northwards the beds then alternate between southerly and near-horizontal dips over the hinge zone of this anticline. The exposure here on the foreshore is seaweed-covered and not easy-going; it is best to view the structure from the seaward side at low tide and to keep to the cleaner exposure under the cliffs to examine detail.

There have been interesting scenarios put together for a river environment for the deposition of these rocks. The beds have become progressively thicker northwards in this section and they contain, locally, concretionary limestones. These latter have been interpreted as the growth of carbonate within soil during periods of subaerial exposure in a semi-arid climate. Some of the large-scale cross-bedding in this sequence, seen as sets of shallow-dipping curved bedding surfaces, are seen as representing meandering point bars in a river system; and generally the rocks represent river channel deposits in a broad meandering river belt and floodplain, while the siltstones we have seen further south, represent fine-grained overbank deposits on the floodplains.

At the end of this section it is possible to scramble up the cliff by one of several rough paths and to join the cliff top path. As you return along this path to the car park you get a good bird's-eye view of the rocks you have been traversing.

7. *Bedding dipping south at locality 4, with cleavage dipping steeply north; figure for scale.*

T. Moelfre

Moelfre is a picturesque former fishing village with a long maritime history. It attracts many visitors to its seafront with its pubs and cafes, and to visit the Lifeboat Station and nearby RNLI Seawatch Centre where there is a small museum and shop. It is at the northern end of the Carboniferous limestone coastline of eastern Anglesey, that forms the cliffs from Lligwy Bay south, to Moelfre, Traeth Bychan, Benllech and Red Wharf Bay. The Carboniferous limestone can be studied at all these places, either directly from the beach or from the coastal path, and different resorts are good for different features. We include this short section at Moelfre, because it shows some of the best examples of recent *karstic* weathering of limestone on Anglesey. There are also fossils, but here they are mostly fragments of *crinoids* and *brachiopods*: coral fossils are better seen at Traeth Bychan.

If you are coming on the A55 from the Britannia Bridge, take the second exit signposted for the A5025 towards Amlwch. After about 25 km, at a small roundabout just outside Moelfre, turn right and drive about 1km into Moelfre village. Following Parking signs left (twice) will bring you to a large free car park with public conveniences [512863]. From here it is a short walk down a path by a stream to the seafront road and the small port of Moelfre where you will need to bear left (N). Take the signed coastal path and after about 200m you reach to the RNLI Seawatch Centre marked by the prominent sculpture of local sailor, Dic Evans [515865]. Alternatively, when driving into Moelfre, keep on the road down to the small port, and then wind uphill out of the village, turning right at the RNLI sign. This brings you to a pay-and-display carpark adjoining the Seawatch Centre and RNLI shop, and affords immediate access to the coastal rocks of interest.

It is possible to access the limestone reefs just below the place where the steps from the Seawatch Centre meet the coastal path [515865]. The limestone beds dip gently seaward, and in the cleaner exposures where the limestone appears palest, you will see that the rock is composed of tiny fragments of shells (brachiopods) and crinoids (Figure 1). Few of the fossils are large or whole, here, but you should see some crinoid tubes 1 or 2cm long, circular in section, and many more separate crinoid ossicles (discs). (See Glossary Figure 2.)

1. Carboniferous limestone on the reefs below the Seawatch Centre, Moelfre. The rock is almost entirely composed of shell and crinoid fragments. The largest crinoid shows its cylindrical shape in side view; others are circular in cross-section. See Glossary Figure 2.

Walk along the coastal path (here metalled) northwards, past the current Lifeboat Station, to the corner by white cottages (Swnt), where the path metalling ends. Here you can easily go onto the flat rocky reefs at [517867], that are part of the broad headland that faces Ynys Moelfre (Moelfre Island) which is usually crowded with seabirds. The reefs of this headland (Figure 2) are popular for sea fishing, providing safe platforms to set up rods and lines. The rocks here are thinly bedded muddy limestones with almost horizontal bedding. They have a rough, lumpy appearance because they are *bioturbated* – ie have been mixed up by burrowing worm-like animals. Some of the paler surfaces reveal that the rock is crammed with fossil fragments, mostly brachiopods and crinoids, as seen in Figure 1.

2. Limestone reefs on the headland at Moelfre looking E. The rocks are thinly bedded bioturbated muddy limestone, giving the lumpy appearance in the foreground. Ynys Moelfre appears far left.

The western end of these reefs forms the edge to a pebble beach and small bay [517868]. The large loose water-worn boulders at the eastern end of this bay, just below the reefs of Figure 2, are the best place to examine the local limestone in close-up. Clean pale grey boulders (Figure 3) reveal sections of shell (brachiopod) fossils and numerous examples of *stylolite* surfaces, that are the characteristic zig-zag dissolution surfaces seen in many limestones worldwide.

3. Examples of brachopod fossils that appear as white crescents in section, and stylolite surfaces that are the dark zig-zag wiggles, in a boulder on the beach near Moelfre. The bedding is vertical in this loose boulder.

Continue along the coastal path, either following it around the headland Eglwys Siglen, which goes past the memorial Hindlea seat, marking the bravery of the local lifeboat crew in saving the lives of all aboard the MV Hindlea that was wrecked in 1959; or take the shorter route cutting inland across this headland. Continue for about 200m; the path first rises over a mound where there is seating, and then descends by steps to take a lower course nearer the clifftop. Look for where the path is close to a prominent corner of a wall, and where a joining inland path is

4. Limestone pavement and karstic features near Moelfre, looking east.
The limestone in the background shows bedding with a gentle southerly dip,
but the foreground is sculpted by erosion to create potholes.

marked with a yellow arrow [514868]. The cliff top just here is the
highlight of this short excursion, showing some of the best karstic
scenery and erosion we have seen on the Carboniferous limestone
coast of Anglesey (Figure 4).

The limestone pavement here, just below the path, is accessible
with care, and it is possible to examine the beautiful sculpted
erosional surface of the limestone over exposures of many tens of
metres. Some potholes are cylindrical holes half a metre deep;
others form interlocking channels and pipes (Figure 4). In detail,
the rock contains fossil fragments and stylolites, not dissimilar to
the loose boulder shown in Figure 3. We are not sure why this
pavement formed just here, or over what period of time, when
most of the limestone in this vicinity has a more normal bedded

appearance (see backround rocks in Figure 4), but we assume this is recent karstic erosion, later than the Ice Age activity seen elsewhere along this coastline.

Return to your car by retracing your steps, or if you have chosen the village carpark, take one of the inland paths that lead you back via pretty cottages, to the picturesque village centre. If you prefer to combine this excursion with a longer coastal walk to Lligwy Bay (a further 2km), you will have many more opportunities to look at the Carboniferous rocks along the way, and would eventually reach the Devonian rocks on the N side of Traeth Lligwy.

U. Traeth Bychan

Traeth Bychan is 2 km to the north of Benllech. It has a wide bay with a sandy beach, framed by cliffs of Carboniferous limestone. The beach is mainly given over to watersports, because the Red Wharf Bay Sailing Club is located here, and there is also a private port on the north side of the bay. The rocks are similar in appearance to the limestones at Benllech 2 km to the south, and Moelfre 2 km to the north, but we consider this the best place to see fossil *coral* communities and *bioturbated* limestone.

Follow the directions to Benllech, taking the A5025 from the A55. Continue on the A5025 northwards through Benllech town, and after about 3 km, immediately after a left turn for the B5110 to Llangefni, there will be a right turn signposted Traeth Bychan. The junction is also marked by a blue cafe sign. Take this narrow

1. *The first exposures in Traeth Bychan looking south: two beds of shelly Carboniferous limestone separated by a thin rubbly bed.*

road either side of which are long-established caravan parks, and after 1 km you will reach the pay-and-display carpark with toilets, on the right side. There is a cafe just below, that you pass walking about 200m down to the seafront. Turn right (south), walking past the sailing club adjoining an old lime kiln, to reach the first low cliffs of limestone (Figure 1). Here there are 2m thick beds of *brachiopod*-rich limestone, with many examples of *Productus* in their original positions parallel to bedding (Figure 2). This is different from the shelly limestone made up of small fragments (bioclastic limestone) that is seen on the Moelfre excursion.

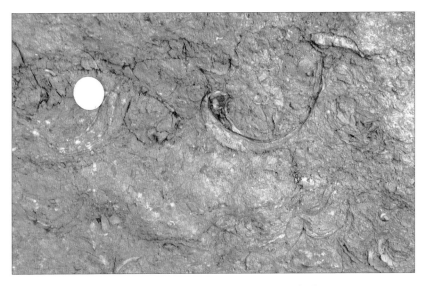

2. Close up view of the limestone in Figure 1, looking west, showing many sections of the brachiopod Productus, *lying parallel to bedding. See Glossary Figure 2.*

Now walk around the top of the beach, past the loose blocks beneath the caravan park that provide some good fossils, until you see the beds of limestone forming sloping shelves below the southernmost caravans (Figure 3) [514851]. It is worth scrambling over the loose blocks to reach these cliff exposures. The clean wave-washed outcrops at the top of the beach and cliff

3. Low cliff exposures S of Traeth Bychan beach that reveal exceptional fossil colonies. Close-up views are shown in Figures 4 and 5.

base reveal beautiful examples of coral colonies with brachiopods, as well as some of the best variegated patterns caused by bioturbation (Figure 4). The prominent ledges above, shown in Figure 5, are the irregular top surfaces of limestone beds almost entirely composed of reef-building corals (Figure 5), and are the highlight of this excursion. At least two types of coral fossils can be seen and are shown in Figure 5: 20-30 cm diameter colonies of *Lithostrotion*, in detail appearing as spaghetti-like tubes of 2-3mm diameter (see also Figure 4); and groups of the solitary horn-shaped coral *Dibunophyllum*, which has a larger diameter of about 1cm. These platforms also reveal the pattern of *joints* seen all along this Carboniferous coast, from Lligwy Bay south to Red Wharf Bay. The two dominant vertical joint sets (Figure 5), approximately E-W and N-S, give a chocolate slab appearance to the rocks, and also create a saw-tooth pattern (in plan) in some of the cliffs between here and Benllech Bay.

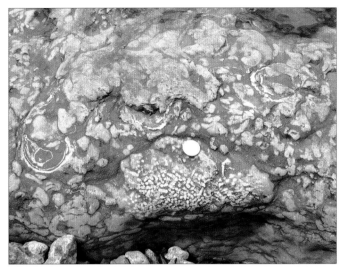

4. Wave-washed base of the exposures in Figure 3, showing a fossil colony of Lithostrotion *and brachiopods, within a highly patterned bioturbated bed.*

5. View of the top of a bedding plane, showing two types of coral. The colonial coral Lithostrotion *is in the central pale grey area, crossed by a joint (see pencil), and the larger circular patterns in the darker grey area just above are the solitary coral* Dibunophyllum. *See Glossary Figure 2.*

V. Benllech Bay

Benllech is the largest seaside town on the eastern shore of Anglesey, and occupies an approximate central position in the coastal outcrop of lower Carboniferous rocks in this part of the island. Traeth Benllech (Benllech Bay) is one of the most popular resorts for beach holidays in all of Anglesey, having a lovely safe sandy beach and plenty of nearby accommodation from hotels to cottages and caravans. Benllech town has a range of shops and other facilities, and the beach road has access to large carparks with public conveniences and a seafront cafe/shop. The coastal rocks surrounding this large bay are Carboniferous limestone with minor shale and the rocks in the cliffs on the south side of the beach are easily accessible from the beach sand.

1. Bedded limestones and thin mudstones, with many joints and a small cave, on the cliffs on the south side of Traeth Benllech. This is a nice locality for children, as our grandsons show.

2. View of the limestone cliffs near to Figure 1, showing smooth grey limestone in the lower section, with pockets of mudstone, thin shale beds above, and then a rough lumpy bioturbated limestone above. Notebook on a bedding plane.

If you are coming on the A55 from the Britannia Bridge, take the second exit for the A5025 signposted Benllech, which you will reach in about 13km. There is a signposted road right, taking you to the seafront; it loops back into town to join the A5025 again, which would be the route to take if coming from the north. At the seafront, park in the pay-and-display carpark next to a cafe and shop; there is an overflow carpark nearby if this is full. Cross to the sandy beach and turn right to walk to the rocks in the cliffs about 100m along the south side of Traeth Benllech [524823] (Figure 1).

The cliffs and their ledges reveal horizontal bedded rocks, with beds of dominant limestone separated by much thinner beds of shale or mudstone. Some of the limestone beds are darker, and have a lumpy appearance, which is caused by *bioturbation* in muddy limestone by burrowing worm-like creatures (Figure 2), that can be seen in exceptional detail on the neighbouring Traeth Bychan excursion. The cliff rocks at Benllech also show many *joints* that are perpendicular to bedding, that weather out to create caves, or create conduits for natural springs (Figure 1). These rocks provide a good combination of geology and opportunities for beach play.

W. Red Wharf Bay

Red Wharf Bay is the largest natural harbour on Anglesey, nearly 5km wide at its maximum. The rocks we shall see are exposed in cliffs and shore platforms on the northwest side of Red Wharf Bay, that separate this bay from Benllech Bay. These rocks are dominantly shelf carbonates formed in the Lower Carboniferous (about 330 Ma), that contain coral and brachiopod fossils, with interbedded sandstones. What makes the area special is the evidence here for episodes of subaerial exposure and erosion in the Carboniferous, producing fossilised *karst* geomorphology with infilled pipes that are rarely seen elsewhere in the British Carboniferous. Red Wharf Bay is also one of only two sites in northern Wales where Quaternary raised beach deposits have been recorded, providing evidence for interglacial conditions and sea level rises during the Pleistocene.

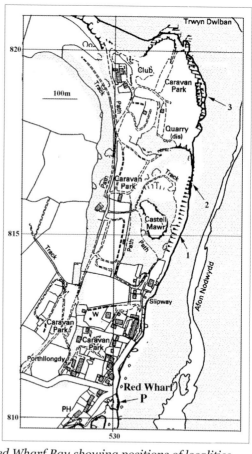

1. *Map of the coast north of Red Wharf Bay showing positions of localities 1 – 3, modified from the 1:10,000 map of the Ordnance Survey.*

The 1 km coastal section has well-exposed cliffs, better not approached too closely because they are soft and unstable. Foreshore beach exposures and platforms are safe and accessible from the beach sand at all but the highest tides, but low tides make access easiest.

From the Britannia Bridge, after 1km take the exit for the A5025 road signposted Benllech. In 7km after passing through Pentraeth, take the narrow minor road on the right signposted Red Wharf Bay. Where the road bends left, go straight on to the bay on an even narrower lane. On reaching Red Wharf Bay [530811], turn right where there is good free parking (Figure 1). It can become full at weekends and in the holiday season, as there is a good beach and a popular restaurant and inn.

Walk out of the car park and along the seafront road northwards (Figure 1), then on to a path with seats (100m). Crude steps to the beach from here take you straight on to the first beach exposures,

2. *View of Red Wharf Bay looking north, with limestone beach exposures in the foreground, and Castell Mawr in the distance.*

wave-washed outcrops of Carboniferous Limestone against the sea wall (Figure 2). The rocks here *dip* gently SE, and contain fossil fragments of shells (*brachiopods*) and *corals*. A prominent feature are vertical *joints* in two distinct sets, the stronger approximately E-W and a weaker set approximately N-S. From here, continue walking along the beach about 500m northwards until you reach cliffs below the prominent Castell Mawr (Figures 1 & 3).

Alternatively, return to the sea front road, and walk northwards past houses, and descend to the beach by the slipway before the end house (Figures 1 & 2). Continue another 200m along the beach to the cliffs below the prominent mound of Castell Mawr, which is the first main locality.

3. View of locality 1 looking SW. In the foreground is the cliff-base outcrop of brown sandstone. The Castell Mawr limestone towers above unstable cliffs of glacial till and quarry spill.

Locality 1: beach exposures below Castell Mawr quarries [532816]

At the foot of the cliff to the north end of the towering limestone cliffs of Castell Mawr (Figures 1 & 3), the first solid rock encountered is an orange-weathered, 2 – 3 m thick sandstone bed (Figure 4). It underlies the dominant limestones that form the prominent feature of Castell Mawr; these limestones were extensively quarried for centuries and used for major building and castles in North Wales.

In the soft cliffs immediately above the sandstone in the prominent cliff-base exposures (Figure 4), patches of conglomerate and breccia can be seen, made up of locally derived limestone, cemented by calcite. These deposits are indicative of a raised beach in the Ice Age; this particular one is considered to be of Mid-Pleistocene age (125,000 years). Patches of rounded cobble (conglomerate) indicate raised beach pebble deposits; areas of angular scree-like clasts (breccia) are suggestive of cliff

4. The sandstone bed at locality 1, looking W, with overlying raised beach deposit immediately above on the left. The more angular rubbly deposit above, in the centre, is a mix of quarry spill and till.

edge or cliff fall deposits (Figure 4). Both types point to a higher sea level compared to present day, creating raised beach platforms and associated beach and cliff-edge deposition. Overlying these deposits is the red-brown Irish Sea *till* that forms the dominant cliff material, although at this locality the cliffs are complicated by quarry spoil, and ridges that indicate cliff subsidence (see Figure 3).

Beneath the orange-coloured sandstone is another limestone, that forms the prominent seaweed-covered wave-cut platform at this location (Figure 4): one of the shore platforms around this part of the coast of Anglesey that are evidence of sea-level rise and associated raised beaches during the Ice Age. Wave-polished limestone beds reveal fossils such as fragments of crinoids and brachiopods, and some silicified coral colonies (*Lonsdaleia duplicata*). Other features of silicification are nodular *chert*, although this is seen better at the next locality. The beds here dip very gently south (see Figure 3), so that as we progress north, we come into older rocks.

We shall be continuing northwards, but to avoid walking on slippery rocks and seaweed in the foreshore, we advise walking along the sandy shore if the tide is low enough. Continue until near the end of the high cliffs, where there is a cave in the limestone (Figure 5).

Locality 2: prominent cave [533817]
This cave (Figure 5, also Figure 1) is the site of a large pipe-like cavity, 3m high and 2m across, now filled with a plug of sandstone from above. This is a foretaste of the next locality, where a larger number of these sandstone-filled pipes at a lower stratigraphic level can be examined in a safer environment. The bulbous plug at the top of this cave, as well as the cave itself, are evidence of sub-aerial erosion and karst formation between the deposition of the limestone beds on tropical shelf seas, and the sand deposition that created the overlying sandstone. The

limestone exposed either side of the cave reveals some prominent strings of chert (silica) nodules; these appear as irregular whitish blobs in the grey limestone (Figure 5). Also seen here are characteristic zig-zag lines that indicate the presence of *stylolites*: a common feature in many types of limestones and evidence of solution and material loss on irregular surfaces that over time become serrated sutures marked by films of insoluble clay minerals.

5. Locality 2: a large pipe has created a cave within the limestone, and is filled by a plug of sandstone from above. To the top-left of the cave, there are strings of chert nodules in the limestone, and below are zig-zag stylolite surfaces parallel to bedding.

Return to the sand and continue northwards on the beach for 200m, and then make your way across slippery seaweed to the low cliff and foreshore exposures beneath a camping field, marked by a prominent low cliff with an overhanging limestone bed (Figure 6).

Locality 3: limestone shore platform and infilled pipes [533818]

This locality (Figure 1) provides access to spectacular sandstone pipes within limestone, that are the fossil evidence of karst scenery during the Carboniferous at this time. The rocks here underlie those seen at Localities 1 and 2. The low cliffs seen in Figure 6 are composed of a 2m limestone bed above, and overhanging, a 1.5m soft mudstone (shale) bed. It is *not* advised to look closely at these beds, because of the overhang and possible cliff falls, but to concentrate on the sandstone rock platform and hummocks in the foreground of Figure 6, and up to 100m northwards into a small bay south of Trwn Dwlban [532820], which is the highlight of this excursion: the limestone pipes and infills.

6. Area of locality 3: limestone overlies mudstone in the cliff, and the figure is seated on a raised beach platform of sandstone. This sandstone feeds down into, and fills, pipes in the underlying limestone, creating the hummocky foreground with prominent sandstone plugs.

167

The raised platform and hummocky foreground of Figure 6 are composed of the sandstone bed that covers and fills pipes and potholes in the limestone beneath. There are several dozen pipes in this vicinity, up to 1.5m across and 3m deep, with walls that taper downwards, generally filled with cream-weathering sandstone. In three dimensions, several filled pipes are seen to be fed from the sandstone immediately above (Figure 6), some up to depths of 5m. Other infilled pipes stand out as eroded remnants, appearing as stumps in their initial upright position, or occasionally to have fallen on their sides (Figure 7). In detail, the infilled pipes and stumps reveal fine layering in the cream sandstone infill, and some contain patches of pebbly infill.

These pipes form unique evidence of emergence and erosion of the Carboniferous carbonate platform, marking periods of

7. Two sandstone plugs that have been revealed by the erosion of the surrounding limestone; the fallen plug in the foreground shows downward tapering towards the viewer.

marine regression (retreat) and aerial emergence of the platform, followed by submergence. During the episodes of emergence in lower Carboniferous times, erosional channels and pipes were formed, similar to potholes and clints and grykes seen on present-day limestone platforms and karst landscapes. These were later submerged and filled with sandstone detritus from flood-generated rivers, that are now preserved as pipe infills up to 3m diameter and 5m depth as seen in Figures 6 and 7.

8. *Small bay showing glacial striae on limestone shore platform, overlain by Irish Sea till in the low cliffs. The striae and ridges run diagonally across the picture (NW-SE) towards the figure standing to the right of two eroded pipes.*

Take a small path at the north end of the shale cliff shown in Figure 6, that in ~50m takes you into a small bay of smoothly polished low limestone exposures (Figure 8) [532820]. This is one of the best examples of a grooved and striated Ice Age shore platform in NW Wales, revealing the direction of ice flow in the Pleistocene. The *glacial striae* on the limestone pavement generally trend NE-SW, in the direction of the m-scale glacially carved ridges seen particularly well in the upper shore outcrops (Figure 8). However, the striae can be seen deflected into the hollows associated with the pipes (Figure 9), suggesting the ice flowed into, and eroded, some of the Carboniferous-infilled pipes, during the Pleistocene. This particular pipe (Figure 9) reveals a remnant plug of harder pebbly sandstone infill, that has survived the glacial erosion that stripped away most of its infill.

This locality is also the best place to see the Red Irish Sea till on this Red Wharf bay section. In the small bay where the glacial striae are seen best (Figure 8), several metres of this till immediately overlie the polished limestone and form the foundation to the camping field. This till is a product of the northwestern incursion of ice from the Irish Sea Basin onto eastern Anglesey in the late Pleistocene glaciation (~18,000 years), near the end of the Ice Age.

9. One pipe from the glacially striated shore rocks in Figure 8, showing striae (scratches) deflected into a pipe, demonstrating that ice flowed into, and eroded, the pipes during the Pleistocene.

X. Lleiniog

This cliff section along the Menai Strait shore to the east of Beaumaris contains Quaternary sediments that present a great variety of fluvio-glacial structures as well as erratics of an extraordinary range of size and composition (Figure 1). The shore below the cliff provides an opportunity to examine the shape, size and composition of the pebbles and boulders derived from the *till* in the cliffs. The section has completely open access.

1. View of the foreshore and cliffs at Lleiniog, looking SW. Two large limestone erratics mentioned in the text are seen at the extreme right, and left of centre (beneath the tree). The sea-stack discussed in the text (Figure 2) is on the extreme left. Limestone erratics derived from the cliff are scattered on the foreshore, but the heap of limestone fragments on the shore in the foreground are probably the collapsed remains of another large erratic.

Immediately after the Britannia Bridge take the first exit from the A55 for the eastbound A4080, signposted to Beaumaris, then at the next roundabout continue on the A545 on to Beaumaris. From Beaumaris go northwards on the B5109 and, after 3km take a right turn on a minor road signposted Penmon, towards the village of Lleiniog. Just as this road turns parallel to shore, enter the large unsigned car park on the right [621792]. Walk back to the road and take the signposted footpath south along the shore. If the car park barrier is too low for your vehicle, there are lay-bys on both sides of the road. The section does require low tide or retreating mid-tide, and like all eroding cliff sections there is the possibility of falling blocks, so care is needed.

The sediments in this section are interpreted to be the product of the streams beneath or in front of a retreating glacier. The composition of the sediments suggests that it mostly originated from the northeast, with some input from Anglesey and the Irish Sea basin. However, the composition of the pebbles indicates that some were the product of reworking of pre-existing glacial sediments, coming from north Wales. The mixture of the composition of the *erratics* suggests a confluence of Irish Sea and Welsh ice immediately northeast of Penmon in the mid-Pleistocene some 24 to 10 million years ago.

There are magnificent sections of Quaternary sediments in the cliff, as well as boulders and pebbles derived from them, seen on the shore below. Irish Sea till overlies *fluvio-glacial* sediments in the cliff (Figures 1-4), both containing an extraordinary variety of erratics. The sediments in the lower sections of the cliff are a mixture of gravels and sands containing small pebbles of a great variety of rock types, mostly from northern Britain, and some locally derived Carboniferous limestone pebbles. Some of the boulders and pebbles are from the lower Palaeozoic sediments and volcanics of north Wales. Locally, there are small coal fragments in the sands, in some places forming distinct beds. These sediments generally display superb sections of large and small-scale cross bedding, channelling and other sedimentary features, as seen for instance in Figures 2-4.

The overlying Irish Sea till has been interpreted as a product of the melting beneath a re-advancing glacier. The lowest levels, at the junction with the gravels beneath, are often marked by a bed with large boulders, especially of limestone, up to 1.5m across, as seen at the right edge of Figure 2; the larger erratics on the beach have been derived from this horizon. In general, *clasts* in the till are 10-20cms in greatest dimension, set in a matrix of clay and sand together with smaller clasts in the range of 2-5cms, all of the clasts being of the same range of composition as those seen in the gravels beneath. These boulders and smaller stones are best seen on the beach below.

2. *The sea-stack at the left-hand edge of Figure 1, discussed in the text. In the lower half are the fluvio-glacial gravels with a wedge of sand to the left. Above, is the till with its larger boulders; one large boulder of limestone protrudes from the right-hand edge; the shore is littered with limestone boulders.*

Most of the general features of the gravels and sands, as well as those of the overlying till, can be seen in the cliff and are superbly displayed for some 500m. However, some specific features are pointed out below, starting from the large limestone erratic you will see about 30m along the shore, on the far right of Figure 1. This is one of two large Carboniferous Limestone erratics that have been derived from the till in the cliff above; it is some 2-3m in diameter, and exhibits bedding (now vertical) that is emphasised by erosional hollows and exceptionally clear glacial striae on the seaward face. On the foreshore below this (see

173

Figure 1) is a pile of angular limestone fragments that may represent the wave-eroded remnants of another large erratic. Further on, on the seaward edge of the upper foreshore, is a second large Carboniferous Limestone erratic (below tree on skyline in Figure 1); this is over 3m in cross-section and 7m long and again exhibits vertical bedding.

The upper foreshore (Figures 1 & 2) is littered with smaller stones and boulders also derived by recent erosion of the material in the cliff above, and are best seen at the left-hand edge of the cliff in Figure 1, on the far side of the sea-stack of Figure 2. These stones vary in size from around 10 to 30cm, the largest being more angular and equidimensional, the smaller smoother and more elongate. They are mostly of Carboniferous Limestone and must have been derived from the limestone that is seen in outcrop a few kilometres to the north on Anglesey. The polished surfaces of the smoother limestone boulders often reveal glacial striations, *stylolites* and *bioturbation* features. Excellently displayed fossils are also seen with *Dibunophyllum*, *Syringopora* and *Lithostrotion* prominent amongst the corals, whilst *brachiopods*, especially *Productus*, and *crinoids* are also common. (See Glossary, Figure 2.)

One interesting boulder is a 50cm-long *porphyritic* pink granite, to be seen on the shore beyond the sea-stack, almost certainly derived from the Shap granite of the Lake District. Otherwise the composition of the boulders and smaller stones here is as seen in the cliffs above – dominantly Caledonian granites 390 million years old, red millet-seed sandstones of Permo-Triassic age (about 250 million), Tertiary (about 50 million) basalt and flint, all originating from the north, as well as *rhyolite*, welded *tuff*, *dolerite*, microgranite, sandstone and slate, all almost certainly originating from north Wales. On the lower seaweed-covered foreshore below this are good, although very slippery, exposures that illustrate the three-dimensional nature of the large-scale *cross-bedding* in the fluvio-glacial sediments.

In the cliff, two remarkable features in the gravels and sands are seen just south of the sea-stack. Figure 3 shows a pair of *faults* affecting beds of gravel, resulting perhaps from the melting of trapped ice beneath. Just north of this, immediately below the junction with the till, are some overturned folds that record movement of the ice sheet above.

In the cliff section, around 30m beyond the first large erratic described above, the junction of gravels and sands with the overlying red-coloured till is seen; this is one of only two places here where the till is accessible. It then rises up 2-3m above the beach and eventually comes down again, after 500m, at the southern end of cliff section, where it is again accessible for a few metres. Although the junction is in some places quite sharp (Figure 4), in others there is a zone where the two units have

3. The fault pair in the gravels and sands to the south of the section in Figure 1.

become mixed, as seen in the sea-stack in Figure 2. Along the contact, the irregular erosional base of the till, resulting from its cutting down into the gravels can be seen, particularly so in the cliff beyond the sea-stack, where there are collapse structures of till into the sediments beneath. This red-coloured till is interpreted as a melt product of a re-advancing ice-sheet; it contains many large boulders of limestone, as well as smaller pebbles, and must be the source of those on the shore below.

About 100m beyond the sea-stack, low down in the cliff face, there are beds of sand up to 4m long and 20cm thick, containing coal fragments locally concentrated in continuous seams. These are considered to be probably derived from a submarine outcrop that is known to lie just a few kms off the northeast shore.

4. Large- and small-scale cross-bedding in the fluvio-glacial sands and the erosional base of the till above.

Y. Beaumaris

This excursion provides a rare opportunity to examine several igneous *dykes* of Caledonian age that have intruded the metamorphic country rocks of Anglesey. The location is adjacent to the beach on the shore of the Menai Straits (Figure 1); at the time of writing access involves a jump or clamber down a metre-high bank, but otherwise the excursion only involves a short walk along a sand and pebble beach to look at 300m of cliff and shore exposures, accessible at all but the highest tide.

1. *View of the Menai straits shore locality looking southwest, showing the first dyke by the figure, and near-horizontal schistose banding in the surrounding schists.*

If approaching from the Britannia Bridge take the A5 at the first exit and then turn right where signposted to Menai Bridge. Continue to a roundabout after 1km, into the town of Menai Bridge and then take the A545, following the signs for Beaumaris. Proceed for about 7km along the narrow winding road to the outskirts of the town, where you can park in a large lay-by just before a large boatyard on the right. Go down on to the beach at the west end of the lay-by and walk for a 100m west to the first cliff outcrop.

The rocks exposed along the coast here are *schists* from the late Precambrian Gwna Formation, that dominate the geology in this SE corner of Anglesey. These rocks are well-seen in a series of cliff exposures for the next 300 metres, as seen in Figure 1. The composition of the schists is of *quartz, feldspar, chlorite* and *muscovite* but it is difficult to determine any indication of bedding. The schistosity is interbanded with quartz knots and veins that give the rock the appearance of a *gneiss* (Figure 2); there are many small-scale *folds* of the *schistosity*, of a few tens of centimetres wavelength, but they show no consistent sense of *overturning*. The schistosity is overall nearly horizontal, although there are a number of sections where it dips nearly

2. Small-scale folds in the Gwna schists, here overfolding to the southwest.

178

vertically, giving rise to metre-scale folds that are overturned both to the SW and to the NE.

The principal interest of this excursion, however, are the Caledonian *dolerite dykes* that cut across the schists. Two representative dykes are seen in the very first exposures; the first is 1.2m-wide, dipping steeply and trending NW (Figure 3), followed west by a vertical 20cm-wide dyke (Figure 4) that shows particularly clear junctions with the schists.

3. The first dyke; figure is pointing to top edge. View looking northwest.

It is interesting that there is no obvious disturbance of the schists at their junctions with the dykes; this raises the question of how was this injection of hot igneous magma achieved? The hot magma must have exploited a pre-existing crack in the country rock and displaced, swallowed or dissolved the rock in its path; if it had just pushed the country aside, we might have imagined that the schistosity would have been disturbed, which is not the case here, as seen in Figures 3 & 4. There is a particularly interesting break in the smaller dyke, seen in Figure 4, with an apparent displacement. It could be a later *fault*, or a change in direction of the intruding fluid. We have to remember that we are only seeing a 2D picture of a 3D process; this is perhaps why the two ends of the break in the dyke apparently do not match.

4. Thin dolerite dyke with the break (top) discussed in the text. The gneissose texture of the schists and mineral lineation on a schistosity surface is shown front-right.

There are some interesting pink carbonate-covered surfaces in the schists of these first outcrops. The carbonate and the enclosing quartz veins are strongly lineated, suggesting that there has been movement, in a NE-SW direction, along some of schistosity surfaces (Figure 4). In all the outcrops there are thin, mm to cm-scale, quartz veins dipping at a variety of angles and cross-cutting the schistosity but not the dykes.

Beyond the first dyke outcrops described above, over a stretch of about 300m to the far end of Figure 1, many more dykes can be seen, generally striking NW, mostly near vertical but dipping at various steep angles. Some of the features to look out for are: thin off-shoots from a thick 'master' dyke, sharp bends where a dyke has followed the trend of the schistosity, *joint* patterns, and displacement by small faults (e.g. Introduction, Figure 8). Near the far end of the exposures, an unusually thick dyke that bounds the SW end of a high cliff wall contains mm-size holes called *vesicles*, where gas has escaped from the magma (Figure 5). Just beyond here, the cliff marked by a graffiti cross that is next to folds in the schist, is a suitable place to end the excursion, and return to the parking place.

5. *Amygdales (gas escape holes) in the centre of a thick dolerite dyke by the wall; pen is 15cm long.*

Glossary

Acadian Orogeny period of mountain building in the Devonian that postdates the *Caledonian Orogeny*

adit an opening or passage into a mine

agglomerate a mixture of coarse angular fragments and finer-grained material formed during a volcanic explosion

anticline an upward closing arch-like *fold*; see Figure 1

axis, fold axis see *folds*

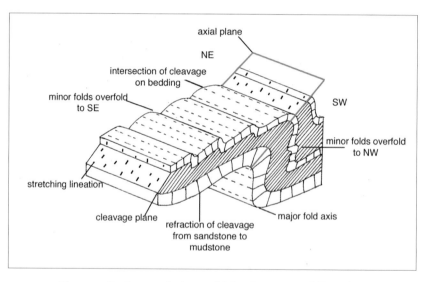

Figure 1. Features relating to folds, cleavage and lineation.

axial-plane the imaginary plane that joins successive *fold axes*, and bisects *folds*, as shown in Figure 1; *cleavage* is often subparallel to axial planes in mudstones and *slates*, when it is called axial plane cleavage

basalt a dark-coloured, fine-grained, igneous rock composed mainly of *plagioclase* and *pyroxene* minerals; it most commonly forms as an extrusive rock, such as a lava flow

biotite a black-cloured mica composed of magnesium, aluminium, silicon, oxygen, and hydrogen, forming sheets that are weakly bound together by potassium ions

bioturbation evidence of mixing or burrowing in sediment by organisms such as worms

bottom structure a general term for sedimentary structures, especially *load-structures* and *flute-casts*, that indicate you are looking at the base of a bed

brachiopods common shell fossils in the Carboniferous such as *Productus*; see Figure 2

breccia as *conglomerate*, but with angular *clasts* in a finer-grained matrix

Caledonian Orogeny the mountain building (deformation and metamorphism) that resulted from the collision of two tectonic plates in the late Silurian: Eastern Avalonia (England, Wales and SE Ireland) and Laurentia (including Scotland and NW Ireland)

chalcopyrite a brass-yellow sulphide of copper and iron

chert a fine grained glassy silica deposit, usually in nodules, also known as flint

chlorite a sheet silicate mineral primarily found in *low-grade metamorphic* rocks from the alteration of clay-rich sedimentary rocks, typically of a pale green colour

clasts fragments, grit to boulder size, in a sedimentary rock

cleavage/schistosity the closely-spaced planes along which *slates*, *phyllites* and *schists* may readily split, as a result of the parallel alignment of platy minerals, especially micas, during *metamorphism*; when parallel to the *axial planes* of folds, is described as axial-plane cleavage

cleavage refraction where *cleavage* passes from fine into coarser-grained rocks, such as from mudstone into sandstone, cleavage is often seen to 'refract', producing a fanning of cleavage about *axial-planes* of *folds*; see Figure 1

conglomerate a sedimentary rock composed of rounded pebbles in a finer grained matrix

corals see Figure 2 for coral fossils found in Carboniferous limestone: *Lithostrotion*; *Dibunophyllum*; *Lonsdaleia*

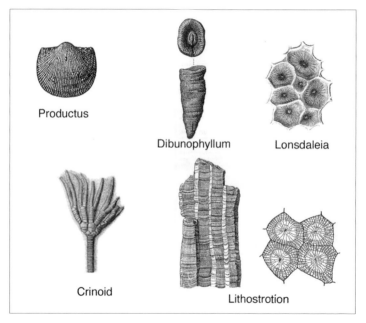

Figure 2. Drawings of typical fossils in Carboniferous limestone: the brachiopod Productus, *a full crinoid, and corals* Dibunophyllum, Lonsdaleia duplicata, *and* Lithostrotion.

crenulation cleavage when an earlier *cleavage* (usually the first-formed) is later deformed, it may be *folded* (crenulated) with an associated new cleavage

crinoid a branching marine fossil, common in the Carboniferous limestone; see Figure 2

cross-bedding or **cross-lamination** a sedimentary structure common in sandstones, where bedding is inclined in sets, deposited as a ripple or dune that indicates current direction; known also as *current bedding*, or on a small scale as *ripple-drift laminations*

current bedding see *cross-bedding*

dewatering structures the expulsion of water from sediments due to loading or shock, resulting in *load structures* at the base of a coarse-grained bed and water escape channels in the overlying sediment

dip the inclination of surfaces in a rock such as bedding planes or *cleavage/schistosity*

dolomite the calcium-magnesium carbonate mineral, $CaMg(CO_3)_2$, or a rock composed of magnesium and calcium carbonate

dolerite a fine-grained basic igneous rock, made up of lath-shaped pale *plagioclase* crystals in a matrix of darker-coloured *pyroxene* and lesser *olivine*, often found as *dykes*

dyke a steep sheet-like intrusion of igneous composition; on Anglesey, these are usually *dolerite* dykes

epidote a commonly occurring mineral in metamorphic rocks, a complex calcium aluminum iron silicate; it occurs here as an alteration product of *feldspar*, usually small crystals, yellowy-green in colour

erratic a rock or boulder that has been transported far from its origin, e.g. by a glacier

fault a fracture that shows measurable displacement of rocks either side: vertical faults may be transcurrent (one side moving left or right laterally); dipping faults may be *normal faults*, with the downthrow down the *dip* of the fault, or *thrusts* if the fault is shallower dipping with the top moving up-dip

feldspar one of the most important rock-forming minerals, aluminium silicates with other compounds: with potassium known as K-feldspar or *orthoclase*, often pink; most commonly with sodium and calcium called *plagioclase*, the latter white

flute cast an erosional hollow on the surface of a fine-grained bed, subsequently filled by the coarse sediment at the base of the next deposit, a useful way-up indicator; see *bottom structure*

fluvio-glacial relates to the water or rivers created by melting glaciers

folds wave-like contortions of layers, with alternating *limbs* connected by curved *hinges*; the line of maximum curvature is the *fold axis*, and the *axial plane* links successive fold axes and bisects the fold; *minor folds* have a characteristic parasitic geometry to larger *major folds*, overfolding towards the major fold axis, as shown in Figure 1

gabbro a coarse-grained intrusive basic igneous rock consisting essentially of *pyroxene* and *feldspar*

galena the principal ore of lead, shiny metallic grey in appearance

glacial striae lines or grooves that have been cut on a rock surface by a glacier

glaucophane a blue mineral (alkali amphibole) indicating high pressure metamorphism, the signature mineral of a blue *schist*

gneiss coarse-grained high-grade metamorphic rock, dominantly *quartz* and *feldspar*

graded bedding a typical feature of *turbidites*, where the coarsest sediment is deposited at the base of the bed, and gets progressively finer-grained upwards

grade see *metamorphism*

granite a widely occurring type of intrusive igneous rock, granular and crystalline in texture consisting mainly of *quartz, mica*, and *feldspar*

graptolites small linear or branching fossils found in shales and mudstones, used for dating especially in British Ordovician and Silurian rocks; *monograptus* is like a saw blade

hinge see *folds* and Figure 1

hornfels fine-grained contact metamorphic rock, showing no preferred orientation of minerals

intersection lineation see *lineation*

isoclinal fold a tight *fold* with parallel *limbs*, like a hairpin in section

jasper red, very fine-grained quartz with inclusions of iron ore

joint a fracture or crack with no lateral displacement (cf *fault*); joints often occur as parallel sets, perpendicular to bedding

karst limestone landform characterised by solution weathering into hollows, or forming a limestone pavement of clints (slabs) and grykes (cracks)

limb see *folds* and Figure 1

lineation *mineral lineation* is an alignment of minerals in *metamorphism*, seen on *cleavage/schistosity* surfaces where it is sometimes called a *stretching lineation; intersection lineation* is the intersection of *cleavage* or *schistosity* on a bedding surface

load-structure a soft-sediment *bottom structure*, where the density/gravitational difference creates a bulbous base; e.g. at the base of a sandstone bed deposited on mudstone

major fold the largest scale fold in an area of interest; see *folds* and Figure 1

melange a jumbled mass of various rock types resulting from sedimentary or tectonic processes

metamorphism changes in mineralogy resulting from changes in pressure and temperature; the *grade* refers broadly to the effect of variations of these conditions, with higher grade meaning higher temperature and pressure

mineral lineation see *lineation*

minor fold see *folds* and Figure 1

muscovite a transparent mica composed of potassium, aluminium, silicon, oxygen, and hydrogen forming sheets that are weakly bound together by the potassium ions, a major component of *schists*

olivine a dark-coloured mineral component of lava and igneous intrusions, composed of oxygen, silicon, magnesium and iron; seen here in *gabbro* boulders, *basalt* lava and *dolerite dykes*

orthoclase see *feldspar*

pillow lava a lava extruded underwater so that chilled skins enclose pillow-like segments; usually *basalt*

188

plagioclase the commonest *feldspar*

plunge the inclination of a *fold axis*, when it is not horizontal

porphyritic describes an igneous rock (e.g. granite, dolerite), that contains some crystals much larger than the rest

pyrite the most common of the sulphide minerals, FeS_2, often found associated with volcanic activity

pyroxene a magnesium-iron silicate often containing calcium and potassium; a constituent of basic and ultrabasic igneous rocks, e.g. *basalt, dolerite, gabbro, serpentinite*

quartz SiO_2, a common rock-forming mineral in sedimentary rocks, as sand grains derived from other rocks; an important component of igneous rocks such as *granite* and *rhyolite*; also found recrystallised in *metamorphic* rocks such as *gneiss* and *schist* and remobilised as quartz veins

quartzite a metamorphic rock almost entirely composed of recrystallised quartz

radiometric date the age of a rock calculated, usually in millions of years, from the radioactive decay of its minerals

rhyolite a light-coloured, fine-grained volcanic rock formed from lavas or intrusions; the mineral assemblage is dominantly *quartz*, with lesser *feldspar* and minor *biotite*

ripple drift lamination see *cross-bedding*

roche moutonnée (sheep's back) is the shape produced by a glacier passing over a rock mound; it is asymmetric, with a smooth *striated* slope and a plucked steeper slope down in the direction of ice flow

schist the product of metamorphism of mudstone (sometimes siltstone) to a higher grade than would produce *slate* or *phyllite*

siderite iron carbonate, $FeCO_3$; sideritic limestone is rich in siderite

sill a sheet of intrusive ignous rock, like a *dyke* but flat in orientation, often parallel to bedding

slate the product of deformation with low *grade metamorphism* of a mudstone, with the production of slaty *cleavage*

sphalerite zinc sulphide, occurrence as *pyrite*

spheroidal weathering a weathering pattern with a rounded crust characteristic of *dolerite dykes*

stretching lineation see *lineation*

stylolites serrated surfaces of dissolution marked by films of insoluble clay minerals, a common feature in limestones; they show up as dark zig-zag traces

subduction a subduction zone is formed where one tectonic plate (commonly an oceanic plate) descends below another plate, forming a trench and usually resulting in *metamorphism* and deformation (orogenesis)

sun-crack structures found in mudstones and siltstones that have been exposed to the sun; useful for identifying the tops of beds that may have been overturned

syncline a downward closing basin-like *fold*; see Figure 1, right-side

tectonic plates the rigid parts of the Earth's crust and upper mantle that collide or move together over periods of geological time; see *subduction* and *Caledonian Orog*eny

tetrahedrite a grey to black metallic sulphide mineral containing copper, iron, and antimony

thrust see *fault*

till also known as boulder clay, a mixture of clay and boulders formed under glaciers and left behind when ice retreats

tuff consolidated volcanic ash

turbidite sediment transported and deposited by density flow, usually fast-flowing ocean-floor currents; characteristically exhibit *graded bedding* and *flute-casts* at their sandstone bases

unconformity the surface between an older sedimentary rock that has been exposed to erosion for an interval of time, and possibly deformation such as tilting of beds or folding, and a younger sedimentary deposit

vesicles bubbles in a volcanic or intrusive igneous rock (e.g. *dyke*), sometimes filled with minerals

zinc blende see *sphalerite*

Other titles about Anglesey from **www.carreg-gwalch.com**

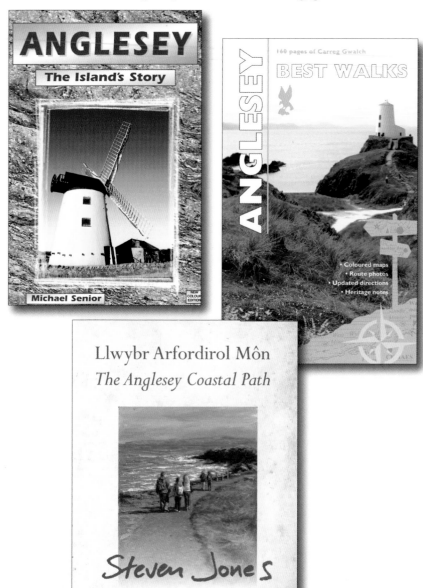